Logic Across the Curriculum

by Michele Best Jackson

illustrated by Pam Boone

FS-10127 Logic Across the Curriculum
All rights reserved–Printed in the U.S.A.
Copyright © 1994 Frank Schaffer Publications, Inc.
23740 Hawthorne Blvd.
Torrance, CA 90505

Table of Contents

Key to Subject Areas

LA = Language, LO = Logic, MA = Math, SC = Science, SS = Social Studies,
GE = Geography, FL = Foreign Language, HI = History

Introduction

To the Teacher:

The puzzles in this book were developed to help students improve the following skills: organizing, gathering data, combining and comparing, ordering, reasoning, interpreting data, thinking critically, and applying problem-solving skills. Each of the puzzles correlates with at least one other area of the curriculum in addition to logic and critical thinking. The activities emphasize patience with problem-solving situations. It should always be stressed that the problem-solving process is much more important than the actual solving of the problems.

The book is divided according to the type of logic skills necessary to solve that particular section. Within each section is a presentation of puzzles that correlate to various areas of the curriculum. These puzzles are offered with the intent that they will be fun ways to build interest before the curriculum is taught in more depth. They may also serve as supplemental ideas that may not be taught as a regular part of the subject due to time limitations.

Preceding each section is a Teacher Tidbit page which gives lesson tips on how to teach learners the problem-solving process for that particular section. "Getting Students Motivated" provides a suggestion teachers may use when short on planning time. The "Steps" section outlines the specific steps of the problem-solving process necessary for each section of the book. These can be combined or further separated, depending on the learning ability and skill level of the students. Finally, there is a "Guided Practice" which suggests an opportunity for students to practice the skills with teacher guidance before attempting them independently.

A good starting point is the page titled "Ride 'em Cowboy." This page allows students to feel successful with deductive reasoning before they actually apply the skill to a puzzle. This will reduce teaching time and frustration and will also raise student success rates if used as a prerequisite to the remainder of the book. Another valuable teaching page is entitled "Tossed Salad." This page should enhance student abilities to use conditional statements. This skill is necessary for students to master the skill of deriving facts from conditional statements, a skill needed to solve the problems presented in the two sections of the book that follow.

The main idea of this book is to add a fun, challenging enrichment to an already existing school curriculum. It should allow students to experiment with and strengthen their problem-solving abilities in a non-threatening, non-graded manner. Good luck to you and your endeavor to teach logic. I hope you and your students enjoy the puzzles and activities included in this book.

Michele B. Jackson

Michele Jackson

TEACHER TIDBITS—Deriving Facts From Statements

GETTING STUDENTS MOTIVATED: To arouse student interest in how to derive facts from given statements, introduce the topic with the following: Imagine you are putting a model airplane together for the first time and all the directions are on separate little pieces of paper and they are not in order. Imagine the frustration you might feel. Often problem-solving can give us a similar feeling. This lesson teaches how to derive facts from statements by asking ourselves questions like what *is* possible and what *is not* possible based on that statement. Since this is the first step in learning how to solve many logic problems, emphasis will be on taking one step at a time.

STEPS:
1. Remind yourself not to panic! We will only do one thing at a time.
2. Carefully read each statement.
3. After you reread each statement (one at a time, of course), list one fact that is not a possibility based on the statement.
   Example: Statement . . . Laura is friends with the cello player.
   Fact . . . Laura must not be the cello player.
4. Repeat listing facts that are not possibilities, one at a time, until all are listed.
5. Reread the statement and list one fact that is a possibility.
   Example: Statement . . . Three boys had pizza while one had a hamburger. Joe is allergic to dairy products.
   Fact . . . Joe must have had the hamburger.
6. Repeat listing facts that are possibilities, one at a time, until all are listed.

GUIDED PRACTICE:
Find six facts from each of the given statements. REMEMBER . . . Concentrate on one fact at a time.

A. Jodi went with Freeman and the oldest brother to see the mud wrestler.
ANSWERS:
Jodi is not Freeman.
Jodi is not the oldest.
Jodi is not the mudwrestler.
Freeman is not the oldest.
Freeman is not the mudwrestler.
The oldest is not the mudwrestler.

B. There were four sisters. Judy is older than at least one person. The youngest sister is a champion swimmer. Ruth is younger than at least two sisters but older than one.
ANSWERS:
Judy is not the youngest.
Judy is not the champion swimmer.
Ruth is not the youngest.
Ruth is not the oldest.
Ruth is not the champion swimmer.
Ruth must be the second to the youngest.

Name_____

Ride 'Em Cowboy

There are four kids from the same school participating in the County Fair Rodeo. Their ages are 8, 12, 13, and 15. Two are females. Gallop through this statement and see if you can lasso 10 facts!

Statement: Black is younger than the calf roper and Blue but older than her boyfriend who is a bronco rider.

1. _____
2. _____
3. _____
4. _____
5. _____
6. _____
7. _____
8. _____
9. _____
10. _____

NOTE: This will not solve a specific logic puzzle. It is a sample fact so that you may practice your fact-deriving skills before attempting an actual puzzle.

COUNTY FAIR
RODEO

TEACHER TIDBITS — Matrix Grid Logic

TOPIC: Teaching students how to mark facts on a matrix grid to solve logic puzzles by the process of elimination.

GETTING STUDENTS MOTIVATED: This topic may be introduced by the following: Think back to the last assignment in logic in which statements were read together and facts listed that were deduced. By taking that activity one step further, you will learn how to chart facts on a grid to solve a logic puzzle using the process of elimination.

STEPS:

1. Carefully read the introduction to the logic problem.

2. Carefully read the first statement to see what is not possible.
   Example: If a statement says "Joan went with Smith to the circus," then you know that Joan cannot be Smith.

3. For each fact that is not possible, locate that space on the grid or chart and place an X in it.
   Example: Statement...Roger is older than Laura.
   Fact...Laura cannot be the oldest.
   Fact...Roger cannot be the youngest.

   Note: Have students copy this sample grid onto scrap paper.

4. Repeat the process, eliminating all non-possibilities for the same statement until they are all charted on the grid.

5. When there is a definite possibility, fill in the entire square which corresponds with the specific fact.
   Example: Michele's age is in between the other two ages listed.
   Fact: Michele must be 16.
   Completely fill in that square.

6. Take a close look at the chart. See if the facts that are charted give you new information.
   Example: If Michele is 16 years old, then Roger or Laura cannot be 16. You can put an X in the Roger/16 box, and you can also put an X in the Laura/16 box.

   Also, if Michele is 16 then she cannot be 12 or 19. Now you can eliminate the Michele/12 box and the Michele/19 boxes by placing an X in each of them.

7. Continue this process until you have gone through all the facts listed. Now go back to the first statement and start over again. The information that has already been entered on the chart will allow you to deduce more facts by rereading the statements.

Example: Reread statement #1. It says that Roger is older than Laura. The only ages left are 12 and 19. If Roger is older than Laura then he must be 19. You can fill in that box and put an X in the Roger/12 box and in the Laura/19 box. Now you can see that Laura must be 12. Continue to mark the boxes appropriately.

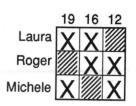

8. As the puzzles become more difficult, many times it is necessary to skip a statement temporarily. When you have read all the statements and charted the facts but still have an unsolved puzzle, go back to statement number one, reread it, and look for new information to be charted.

9. Once students have mastered the simple process and can easily solve a simple puzzle, introduce the idea of cross-referencing. This last step may be taught as a separate lesson and reinforced with practice to raise the student's comfort level and success rate.

   If a = b, and b = c then a must = c.
   Example: If Raleigh is the capital of North Carolina, and North Carolina is the Tar Heel State, then Raleigh must be located in the Tar Heel State.

10. Continue to read the chart and make cross-references to find new facts as explained in the prior steps until the puzzle is solved.

   HINT: Remind students never to make assumptions based on sexual or racial stereotypes!

GUIDED PRACTICE: Give students a copy of the page titled "Stars and Stripes Forever." This activity will help students successfully solve the puzzle using a step-by-step approach. There are hints included to help students establish a system or pattern for solving the puzzle. The puzzle should be completed by individuals with specific teacher guidance.

Toward the end of this section the puzzles tend to get quite difficult. Encourage students to make charts or tables to organize information they know to be factual. This will eliminate frustration. This is not recommended until the cross-referencing ability has been mastered. Your specific objective should determine whether you encourage chart usage or not.

The example shown below can be used with "Capital Punishment" on page 14.

State Name	North Dakota	West Virginia	Montana	Louisiana
Capital				
Nickname				
Year Admitted to U.S.				

Yo Tengo Hambre

Natasha was studying her Spanish and she learned that this means, "I am hungry." It took her some time to figure this out, and when she finally did, she was hungry. In the chart below you will see names of foods in Spanish and English. Chew your way through the facts and help Natasha match each English word with the right Spanish translation.

	El queso	El pollo	La manzana	El tocino
Apple				
Cheese				
Bacon				
Chicken				

Facts:
1. La manzana is not any type of meat.
   That means manzana cannot be _____ or _____.
   Place an X in those boxes.
2. The two meats in Spanish are el pollo and el tocino.
   That means el pollo cannot be _____ or _____.
   It also means el tocino cannot be _____ or _____.
   Place Xs in those boxes.
3. The word apple in Spanish has a "z" in it.
   This means apple must be _____.
   Fill in that box.
4. Pollo is not bacon.

Name_____

This Is the Life

Mr. Sly Fox had his class howling with disbelief when he told them that there are animals in the world that have less than 24-hour life spans. Hop through these facts and use logical thinking to figure out which average life span belongs to each animal listed below.

	14 years	22 years	40 years
Zebra			
Hippo			
Jaguar			

Note: These estimates were based on animals in captivity.

Facts:
1. The animal that lives an average of 14 years does not have a *z* in the correct spelling.
2. The youngest average life span is not that of the hippopotamus.
3. The zebra's average life span is longer than one animal listed but shorter than the other.

Name_____

Funny Bones

Think about a time when you have hit your elbow on something and it felt strange. Sometimes it makes people feel like they want to laugh and cry at the same time. Often people will say, "Oh . . . no! I just hit my funny bone." Did you know that there is no such thing as a funny bone? There are other bones that we identify with a name other than the name a doctor would use. Complete the chart below using logic to find out the real names of these bones found in our bodies.

	Patella	Clavicle	Scapula	Tibia
Shin				
Collar				
Kneecap				
Shoulder				

Facts:
1. The clavicle is above the patella and the shin bone.
2. The kneecap is below the clavicle and it is not called the scapula.
3. The shoulder blade is very near the clavicle.
4. The scapula is not the shin bone.

FS-10127 Logic Across the Curriculum

Name_____

You Must Have Been a Beautiful Baby

Carissa and Mandy were stumped by their teacher. He told them that if they could figure out what kind of animal was a mother to a cygnet, he would take them to the zoo to see the baby joey. They did not know if they should be excited or not because they did not even know what a joey was. Use logic to help Carissa and Mandy figure out the names of these baby animals by utilizing the chart below.

Facts:

1. The cygnet and the kit can live in water; however, the joey and baby turkey cannot.
2. The kit cannot be called an "ugly duckling."
3. The kid has four legs but does not hop or swim regularly.

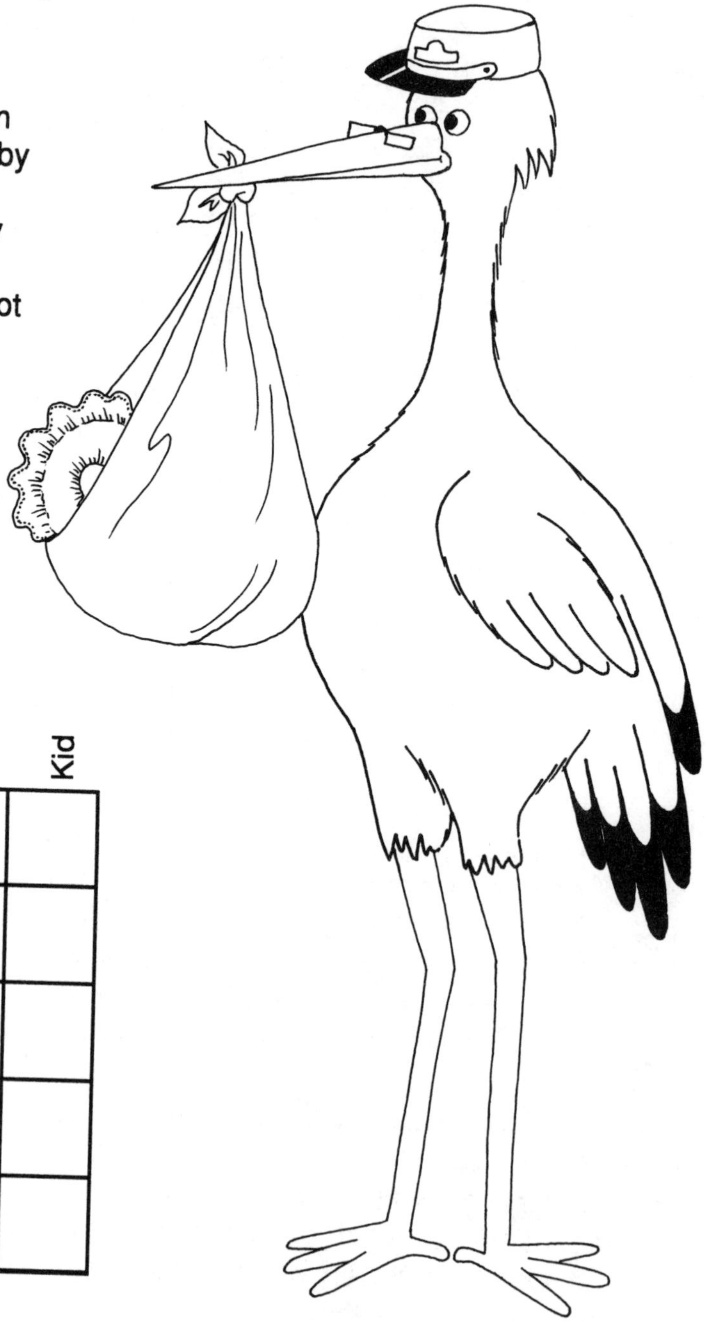

	Cygnet	Pault	Kit	Joey	Kid
Kangaroo					
Turkey					
Goat					
Swan					
Beaver					

Name_____

America or Bust!

An immigrant is someone who is born in one country and then changes his or her citizenship to another. Between 1820 and 1920 approximately 31 million people immigrated to the United States looking for a better life. These people came from all parts of the world. The puzzle below will give you a little more information about the Irish, the Jews, and the Italians that immigrated to the United States between 1820 and 1920. When you have logically solved the puzzle, you will know how many million came and for what reasons.

	Potato crop Failure	Religious Persecu-	Poverty/ Overpopula-	4 1/2 m.	2 1/2 m.	1 1/2 m.
Irish						
Italian						
Jews						
4 1/2 m.			
2 1/2 m.			
1 1/2 m.			

Facts:
1. There were more Italians than Jews who arrived in those years.
2. The Italians and another group of 1 1/2 million immigrants were not persecuted for religious beliefs.
3. More Jews immigrated than the people who immigrated due to potato crop failure.
4. The Irish and the group that was being persecuted for religious beliefs found a new start in the United States even though they faced new problems here.
5. There were more than 1 1/2 million who immigrated due to overpopulation.

Name_____

Let's Communicate

Remember back in second grade when you made a phone with two cans and a long piece of string? It might seem silly looking back at it, but it actually is a pretty good idea. Many of the devices which help us in communication seemed unusual and impossible when they were first invented. In the puzzle below you will learn about some important communication inventors, what they invented, and in what year.

	Telephone	Phonograph	Camera	Transistor	Telegraph	1948	1876	1948	1877	1840
John Bardeen										
Samuel Morse										
George Eastman										
Thomas Edison										
Alexander Graham Bell										
1948										
1876										
1948										
1877										
1840										

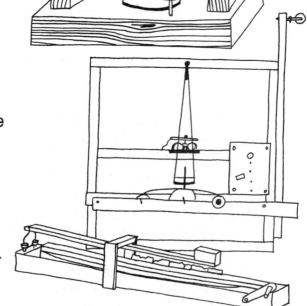

Facts:
1. The phonograph was invented after the telephone.
2. Thomas Edison and the inventor of the telephone made their inventions one year apart.
3. The inventor of the transistor and George Eastman were successful in the same year.
4. Of these inventions listed, Samuel Morse's was the earliest while the camera was one of the last two.
5. Alexander Graham Bell did not invent the transistor.

Elementary, My Dear Watson!

The periodic chart lists all the elements that have currently been discovered. Each element has a chemical symbol and an atomic number. The atomic number is equal to the number of _____ found in one atom of the element. The atom also has electrons and neutrons. The neutrons are located in the _____ of the atom. The protons have a _____ charge and the _____ remain neutral.

Use the information and chart below to separate this mixture of numbers and letters to deduce which of these unusual chemical symbols correlates with the appropriate element and atomic number.

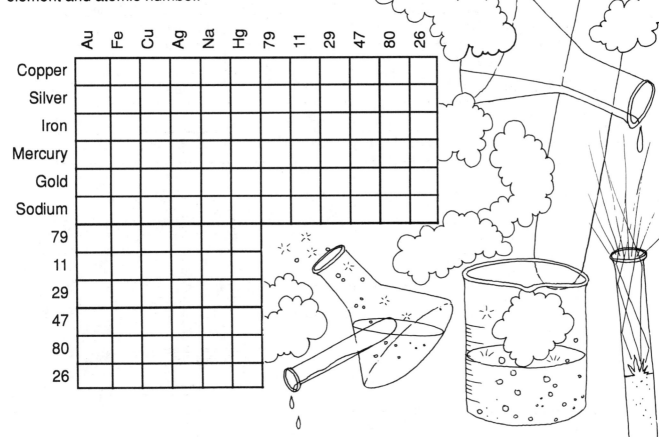

1. The symbols for gold and silver both start with the same letter.
2. The atomic numbers for iron and Cu are higher than at least one other and lower than at least one number.
3. Mercury and Au are right next to each other on the Periodic Table of Elements. The elements are listed by consecutive numbers.
4. Sodium and Hg have the highest and lowest atomic numbers in this puzzle.
5. The difference between copper and Fe is three atomic numbers.
6. Cu has an atomic number that is lower than three others. Ag's number is higher than three of the numbers shown.
7. The atomic number for Mercury is not 79.
8. Fe has 26 protons. The symbol for gold is not Ag.

Name_____

Thanks for the Gumball, Mickey!

No matter what language you speak, it is always important that you know how to say *thank you.* Use logical reasoning and the statements below to match the foreign languages with the appropriate phrases to say "thank you" and "yes."

1. Whether you say *thank you* in Japanese or Swahili, you will start the word with the same letter.
2. *Yes* is spelled the same in Dutch and German.
3. *Arigato* and *Hai* are the same language but *Dziekuje* and *Ja* are not.
4. The first four letters of *thank you* are identical in Dutch and German.
5. *Obrigado* and *Kane* are not the same language nor are they Swahili or Polish.
6. Swahili, *Arigato*, and *Ja* are not generally spoken in the same country.
7. *Yes* in German and Russian has only two letters; but in Japanese, Portuguese, and Polish it has three letters. *Thank you* in Dutch has four letters.
8. *Obrigado* (thank you) and *Tak* (yes) are spoken in different languages that both start with the same letter.
9. *Hai* is not Portuguese or Polish but *Obrigado* and *Dziekuje* are.
10. *Asante* and *Da* are not the same language but *Dank* and *Ja* are, and *Spasibo* and *Da* are also.

Name_____

Gentlemen, Start Your Engines!

The Industrial Revolution brought many cultural, political, and social changes. Becky and her brother Ben became very interested in the subject after watching a documentary. They decided to study it further. They were especially fascinated by the different machines operated by steam. Use logic and the statements below to find out their favorite types of steam machines, who invented them, the inventors' nationalities, and in what years the inventions were made.

Statements:
1. James Watt and the American both presented their inventions before the steam locomotive.
2. John Fitch presented his invention after the Scot presented his, but before 1804.
3. The steamboat was not introduced in 1760.
4. Fitch became famous before the Englishman.

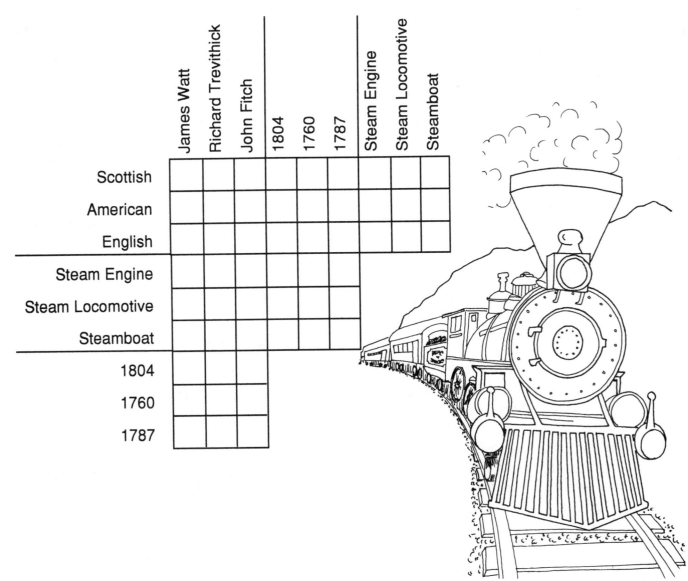

Name_____

Capital Punishment

Lucas's class was playing a game. The class loved this game which was called the "State's Race." The students worked in groups to see who could name the most U.S. state capitals. Lucas, Joshua, and Caleb despised the game because they kept mixing up the states and their capitals. They jokingly called the game "capital punishment." Help the guys figure out these states' capitals, nicknames, and dates of official admission to the United States.

1. West Virginia was admitted before the Treasure State.

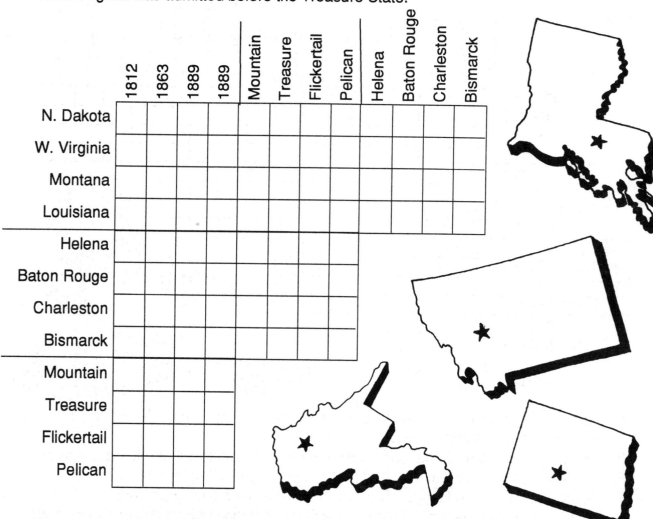

2. Montana and the Flickertail State were admitted in the same year.
3. The Mountain State was admitted after the state whose capital is Baton Rouge.
4. Helena's state and North Dakota were admitted in the same year which was after the Pelican State was admitted.
5. The Treasure state was admitted the same year as the state whose capital is Bismarck. This was after West Virginia.
6. Baton Rouge's state was admitted before West Virginia.

       FS-10127 Logic Across the Curriculum

Name_____

All in Favor Say "I"

Four sisters, Nonet, Rauchelle, Cheree, and Genee were playing a Bingo game. They were not playing ordinary Bingo, they were playing with facts about states that start with the letter *I*. To make it really ridiculous, they did not yell "Bingo," they yelled "All in favor say *I*." Once you have deduced all the facts, you will know each state, its flower, tree, bird, and one interesting point about it.

	Goldfinch	Cardinal	Bluebird	Cardinal	Peony	White Oak	White Pine	Oak	Crystal Ice Cave	Raggedy Ann	Shortest Railroad	Skyscraper	Tulip	Violet	Wild Rose	Syringa
Indiana																
Illinois																
Iowa																
Idaho																
Tulip																
Violet																
Wild Rose																
Syringa																
Raggedy Ann																
Crystal Ice Cave																
Shortest Railroad																
Skyscraper																
Peony																
White Oak																
White Pine																
Oak																

1. Neither Iowa nor the bluebird state has a tulip or violet for a state flower; one of them does have the shortest railroad.
2. The state with the wild rose and Illinois both have a type of oak for their state trees.
3. The skyscraper state and the bluebird state both have a "white" tree.
4. Neither Idaho nor the Raggedy Ann state has the oak as the state tree.
   Hint: Look at statement #2. If the state with the wild rose has an oak tree then Idaho cannot have which flower? Also, is it possible for Illinois to be the Raggedy Ann state?
5. Neither Iowa nor either of the cardinal states has a pine tree.
6. The Raggedy Ann state does not have the pine tree but it does have the tulip for a state flower.
   Hint: Look at the grid. So far, you should have already marked that two states are not the Raggedy Ann state, this means they also cannot be the_____(flower) state.
7. The shortest railroad cannot be found in a "cardinal" state or Idaho.
8. The gold finch and the white oak do not belong to the same state.

 FS-10127 Logic Across the Curriculum

Name_____

How's the Weather?

Think about a time when someone may have asked you "How is the weather where you live?" Often, what they really mean is "How is the climate?" The weather is what is happening on a daily basis and the climate is the average weather over a long period of time. The challenging puzzle below is about climate. When you have used logic with each of the statements below, you will know the average springtime precipitation and the average summer and winter temperatures of four different cities located in Alaska, Minnesota, Mississippi and Nebraska. Warm up to the facts and start deducing!

	Duluth	Juneau	Lincoln	Jackson	Winter 60°	36°	31°	21°	Precip. 17"	8"	8"	15"	Summer 63°	86°	92°	73°
Alaska																
Minnesota																
Mississippi																
Nebraska																
Summer 63°																
86°																
92°																
73°																
Precip. 17"																
8"																
8"																
15"																
Winter 60°																
36°																
31°																
21°																

1. Duluth and the city in Nebraska have the same amount of precipitation in the spring; however, the winter is colder in Duluth.

2. The town in Minnesota has the coldest average temperature in the winter (believe it or not) while Jackson has the highest average summer temperature.

3. Juneau is not in Minnesota or Mississippi but it does have the most precipitation in the spring.

4. The city in Minnesota averages 8" of rain in the spring while the city with a summer average temperature of 92° gets 15".

5. The city that is 36° in the winter averages 86° in the summer. This city is not Duluth and is not located in Alaska.

6. The warmest winter temperature is in Mississippi while the coolest summer temperature is in Alaska.

TEACHER TIDBITS — Picture Logic

TOPIC: Teaching students to solve logic problems in which a picture is necessary to complete the deductive reasoning.

GETTING STUDENTS MOTIVATED: Tell students to think back to a time when they were trying to explain something to another person and the other person did not understand the explanation. Generally people will say, "I need to see it to know what you are talking about." Explain that today's lesson is about solving logic problems in which looking at a specific picture, map or diagram is necessary to assure proper placement or identification of a location or object.

STEPS:
1. Read the introduction carefully.
2. Look at the picture given. Pay attention to clues.
   Example: If one thing stands alone or if an object is unusual in any way.
3. Read Fact #1. Decide if the information given is specific enough to use at this time.
   Example of usable information: The organ pipe cactus has only one other plant next to it. This fact tells you that it must be at either end of the picture.
   Example of non-usable information: The whale shark is pictured next to the tiger shark. This information does not help you at this time.
4. If you decide that a fact is specific enough to use immediately, lightly indicate on the picture the possible location of that specific piece of information.
   Example:

   X   X   X   X   X   X

   Organ Pipe   Organ Pipe

   If the fact is not usable at this time, go to the next fact and continue the reasoning process.
5. As you continue through the process you may deduce that something you wrote in pencil as a possibility is no longer possible. When this occurs eliminate that answer by crossing it out. This should open up new information.
   Example: The organ pipe cactus is to the right of the barrel cactus from your point of view. If it is to the right of something then it cannot be on the far left. You can now eliminate this fact.

   X   X   X   X   X   X

                                                  Organ Pipe

6. When you have read through all the facts and charted the specific information, go back to number one and start the process over again. Now that some facts have been written in, other facts will become more obvious. Continue this process until the entire puzzle has been solved.

Name _____

Say Aaahhh!

Most of us cringe when we hear a dentist say these dreaded words. As any dentist will tell you...the better care you take of your teeth, the more pleasant your dental visits will be. Basically, there are four types of teeth in your mouth. Use logic to identify them.

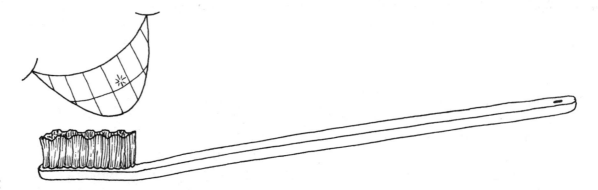

Facts:

1. The premolars are located between the canine and the molars. Hint: Look at the picture closely. If the premolars are between others, they cannot be in section ___ or ___, so they must be in section ___ or ___. Write that lightly in pencil.

2. The canine is located between the premolars and the incisors. That means the canine has to be section ___ or ___. Also, now you know the canine and the premolars cannot be in sections A or D. That means sections A and D can only be the _____ or the _____. Lightly pencil that in by the appropriate section.

3. The molars are not located in front of the mouth. This means the molars cannot be in section ___ so they must be in section ___. Finish the puzzle. If you are stuck, go back to fact #1 and start again.

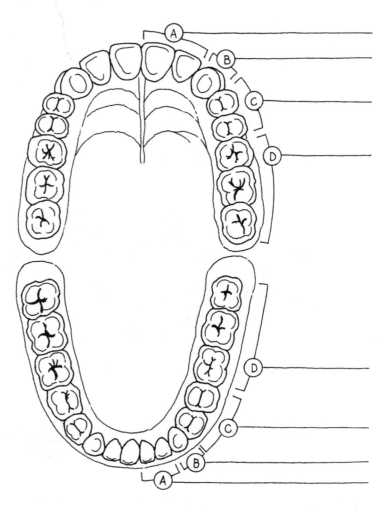

Name_____

That's a Lot of Water!

As you have learned in lower grades, rivers have many uses including irrigation, transportation, electricity, and sustaining life. Do you know what the longest river in the world is? You will if you solve this logic puzzle! Use the graph below with deductive reasoning to learn how many miles long the Chang, Amazon, Mississippi, and Nile Rivers are.

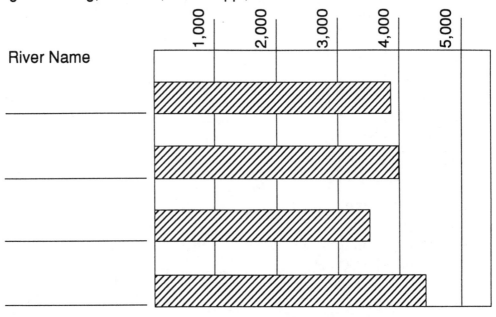

River Name

Length in Miles

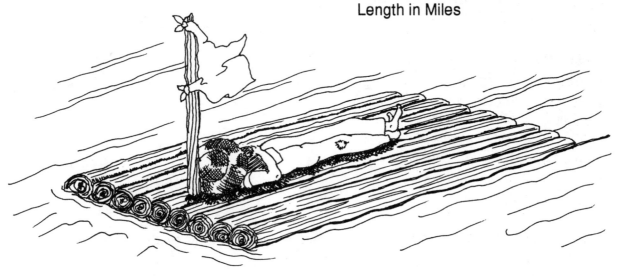

1. The Amazon is longer than at least two other rivers on the graph.
2. The Mississippi is not as long as the Chang River.
3. The Nile is not the shortest river on the graph.
4. The Chang is shorter than at least one other river listed and longer than at least one other river listed.
5. The longest river in the world is not the Amazon.

19

Name_____

Where in the World?

When people hear about the United States they often dream of seeing the Statue of Liberty. It is one of the most famous monuments in North America. Use logic and the picture below to identify where these other monuments are located.

*The display of monuments above bears no resemblance to their relative location to one another in the real world.

1. In this picture, the monuments in Pisa, Italy, and Athens, Greece, each have one other monument touching them.

2. The monument in Delhi, India, is shown between the two Italian monuments.

3. The monument in London, England, is somewhere to the left of both Italian monuments.

Name _____

Mom, I'm Movin' Out!

Lisa and Melissa are celebrating the birth of their new baby brother. After nine months of waiting they finally got to meet the little fellow. The whole event made them curious about the gestational periods of animals. The bar graph below serves two purposes. The first part which is completely filled in shows the average months of gestation. The continuation of each bar, indicated by Xs, indicates the length of time the mother cares for the youngster before letting it "move out" on its own. Use logic to place the bear, bobcat, deer, elephant and seal beside the appropriate bar on the graph.

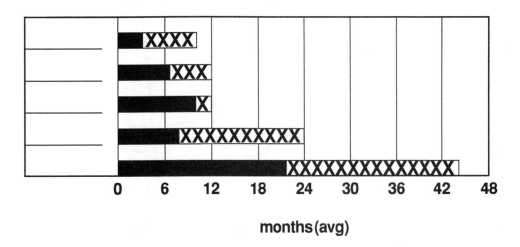

months (avg)

Length of pregnancy ▉

Length of time parents care for young ⌈XXX⌋

1. The bear has a shorter gestational period than the seal but the mother and cub stay together longer than the seal pup and mom.
2. The bobcat has the shortest gestational period.
3. The elephant stays with its mom longer than the bear cub.
4. The deer and the seal both "leave home" at about 12 months.

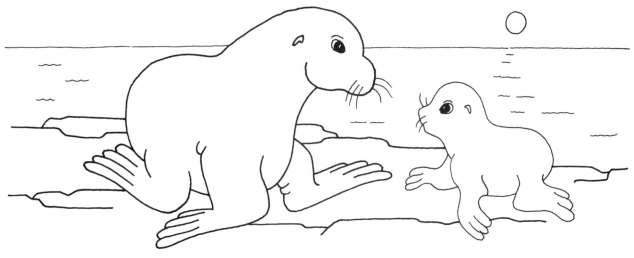

21   FS-10127 Logic Across the Curriculum

Name_____

Flying High

Colt and Russell found some miniature flags when they were cleaning out their garage. They know these flags represent Ethiopia, Italy, Sweden, France, Ireland, and Hungary, but they do not know which flag corresponds with which country. Please color each flag section the corresponding color (ex: color all the *r* sections red), and use the statements below to help Colt and Russell match each flag with the appropriate country.

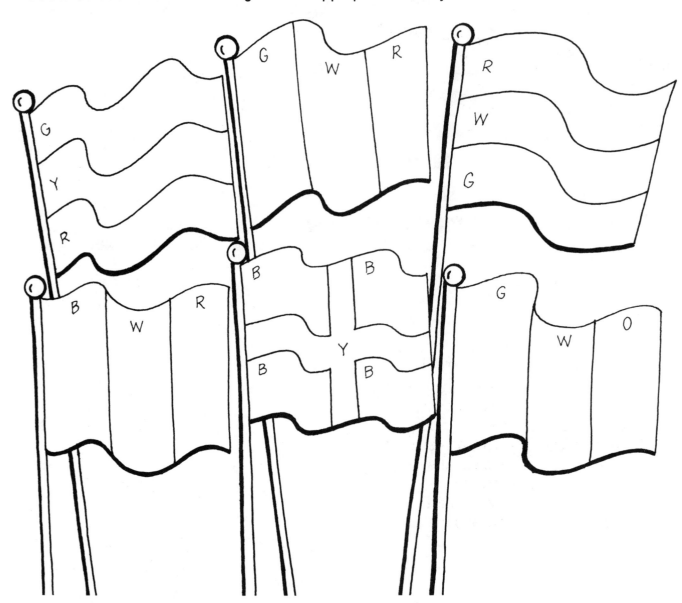

1. Ethiopia, France, and Sweden have either blue or yellow in their flags and one of them has both colors.
2. Ethiopia and Hungary both have a red horizontal stripe.
3. France and Italy both have a white vertical stripe. They also each have a red vertical stripe.

Name_____

Flex It!

Without your muscles, you would not be able to move. There are muscles throughout your entire body. Solve the logic puzzle below to locate six different muscles.

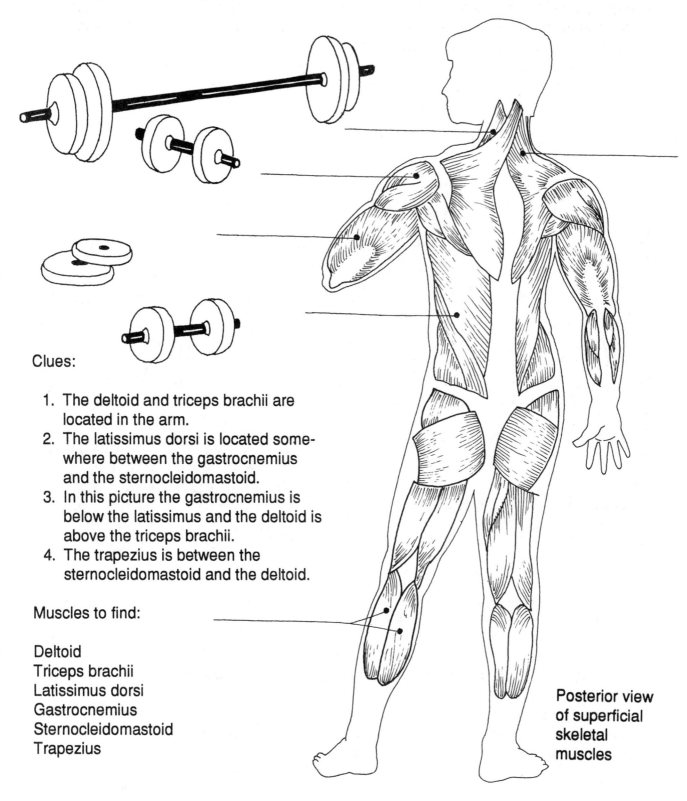

Clues:

1. The deltoid and triceps brachii are located in the arm.
2. The latissimus dorsi is located somewhere between the gastrocnemius and the sternocleidomastoid.
3. In this picture the gastrocnemius is below the latissimus and the deltoid is above the triceps brachii.
4. The trapezius is between the sternocleidomastoid and the deltoid.

Muscles to find:

Deltoid
Triceps brachii
Latissimus dorsi
Gastrocnemius
Sternocleidomastoid
Trapezius

Posterior view
of superficial
skeletal
muscles

Name _____

Ouch!

That is what an unsuspecting person might say if he or she touched a cactus. Cacti grow abundantly and naturally in the Southwest and are loved for their natural beauty, especially when they are in full bloom. Pictured below are some types of cacti. Use logical reasoning to label each specific cactus.

Cacti pictured: aloe, ocotillo, jumping cholla, barrel, yucca, prickly pear, saguaro.

1. The prickly pear and the barrel have two other species between them in this picture.
2. The cholla is between the barrel and the ocotillo.
3. The aloe is between the prickly pear and the saguaro.
4. The ocotillo and the yucca only have one other species to one side.
5. The saguaro, which is usually the tallest in the desert, depends on the Mexican freetail bat to pollinate its beautiful flowers.
6. From your point of view the cholla is somewhere to the right of the saguaro.

Note: In Spanish, a double *l* (as in cholla) is pronounced like a *y*.

24

Name_____

Clickety Clack

Stefanie heard a weird noise in her attic, a kind of clickety clack sound. She went up to see what it was. A tiny window was open. The wind was blowing just hard enough to make her dad's model skeleton move around. First she was scared, but then she started laughing. This grabbed her interest in the human body and the names of different bones. Knock around the facts and see if you can label the pelvis, femur, humerus, sternum, tibia, clavicle, and the radius.

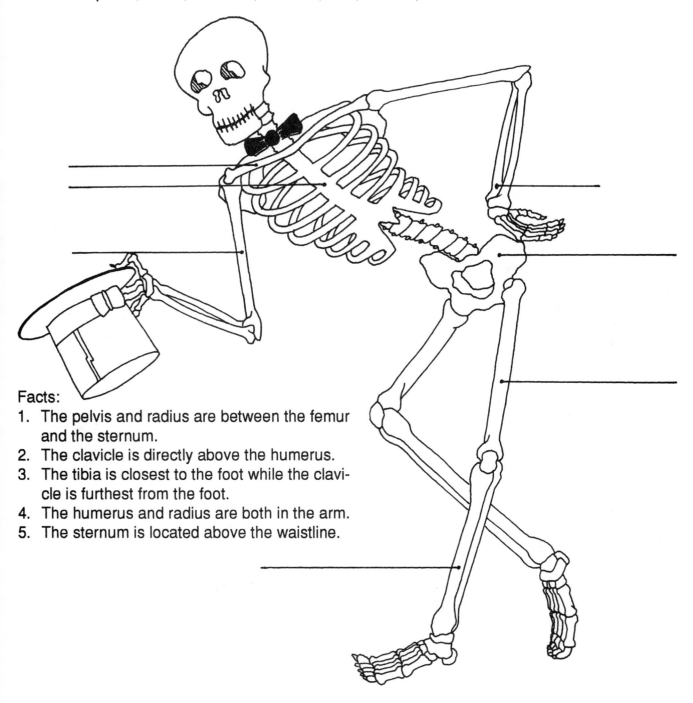

Facts:

1. The pelvis and radius are between the femur and the sternum.
2. The clavicle is directly above the humerus.
3. The tibia is closest to the foot while the clavicle is furthest from the foot.
4. The humerus and radius are both in the arm.
5. The sternum is located above the waistline.

¡Viva la Conquistadores!

The conquistadores came to North and South America to conquer new lands for Spain and to find gold for themselves. Among these men were Ponce de Leon who was looking for the Fountain of Youth and Hernando de Soto who sought the Seven Cities of Gold.

Get out crayons or colored pencils. Use the color-coded key to color the map routes and use logic to match these Spanish explorers with the appropriate map routes.

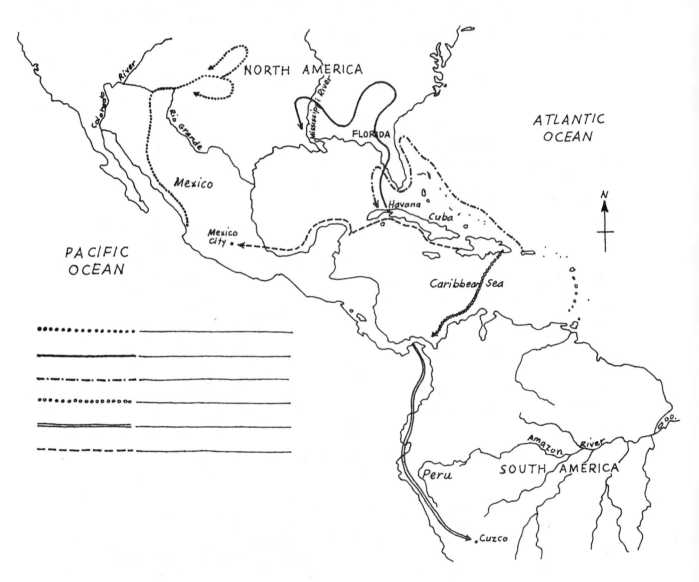

1. De Soto and Ponce de Leon both made it to what is now Florida.
2. Pizarro and Coronado went further north and further south than the other explorers.
3. Cortes explored an area a bit north of where Balboa explored.
4. Coronado and de Soto went further into what is now the United States than the other explorers.

Name_____

Stars and Stripes Forever

Independence! Religious freedom! Freedom from British rule! After studying the American Revolution in social studies, Leah and Heather learned not to take their freedom for granted.

As they made a map of all the battle sites, they learned that many, many lives were lost at the price of fighting for freedom from England.

Closely study the map and figure out where some famous battles between the Redcoats and the American colonists took place during the late 1700s.

1. The battle at Yorktown was north of North Carolina but south of Saratoga.
2. The battles at Charleston and Lexington and Concord were located between the northernmost and southernmost battle sites on this map.
3. The battle at Charleston was located between Savannah and one other battle.
4. Camden was not the southernmost battle.
5. The battle at Yorktown was south of Lexington and Concord and Saratoga.

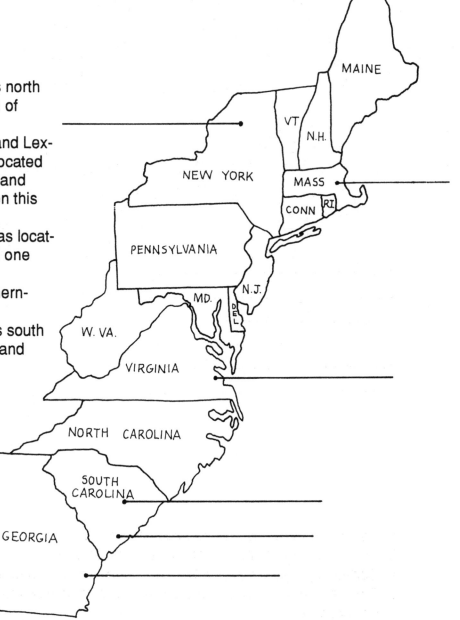

Name_____

Relax, There's Plenty of Time

As you know, the earth rotates allowing the sun to shine directly on an area at any given time. At any location on earth, when the sun is highest overhead it is exactly 12:00 noon at that location. Since there are 24 hours in a day, the earth is divided into 24 time zones. Use logic to match the clocks below with Anchorage, Berlin, Honolulu, Sydney, London, Tokyo, and Rio de Janeiro if it is 12:00 noon in New York City.

2:00 a.m.   7:00 a.m.   12:00 p.m.   5:00 p.m.   3:00 a.m.

2:00 p.m.   6:00 p.m.   7:00 a.m.

1. The Rio clock only has one clock beside it.
2. Anchorage and Tokyo are somewhere to the left of New York City from your point of view.
3. Rio, Berlin, and Honolulu are the clocks in the bottom row.
4. The time in Sydney, Australia, is one hour later than in Tokyo, Japan.
5. Honolulu and Anchorage are in the same time zone.

Name_____

Space Cowboy

The Sun is a ball of extremely hot gases. The solar system consists of the Sun and the bodies that move around it. The planets are the nine large bodies that orbit the Sun. Use logic to correctly label the planets below.

1. Saturn is next to Uranus.
2. Earth is between Mars and Venus.
3. Pluto and Mercury are the closest and the furthest from the Sun.
4. Neptune is between Pluto and Uranus. They are all three very far from the Sun.
5. Jupiter is between Mars and Saturn.

Name_____

Chess Stress

Eight students participated in the annual ninth grade chess tournament. There was a lot of stress because it was a single elimination tournament. In other words, once you lost a game, you were out of the tournament. Use the facts and logic to fill in the tournament chart.

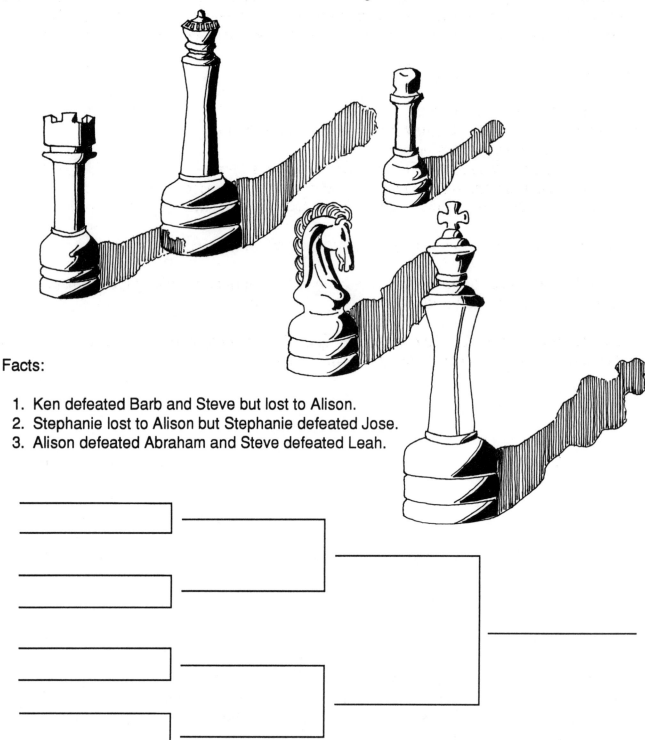

Facts:

1. Ken defeated Barb and Steve but lost to Alison.
2. Stephanie lost to Alison but Stephanie defeated Jose.
3. Alison defeated Abraham and Steve defeated Leah.

TEACHER TIDBITS — Visual Patterns

TOPIC: Teaching students how to distinguish a visual pattern and to follow that pattern to solve a puzzle.

GETTING STUDENTS MOTIVATED: Tell students to imagine that they are private detectives who have been assigned to explore a series of bank robberies. Ask them to brainstorm what types of things they would do to begin their investigation. Lead them toward a discussion about the idea of how to examine patterns in the crimes. Explain that looking for patterns is an essential skill in crime fighting, scientific work, and many other occupations.

STEPS:

1. Carefully read all directions.
2. Identify exactly what the object of the puzzle or problem is.
3. Look at the entire picture or page.
4. Look at each piece of the puzzle or picture one at a time.
5. Try to establish one pattern or sequence between two pieces or pictures.
6. Continue following the pattern with trial and error until you have solved the puzzle.

HINT: If you need extra help, cut out the puzzle pieces and manipulate them.

GUIDED PRACTICE: Have students cut out the die pattern on the next page. Allow them to use it as a manipulative tool when beginning to recognize patterns.

EXTRA: The "cut out" puzzles can be photocopied on colored paper and then laminated to be kept permanently. These make great learning center items.

Name_____

Die Pattern

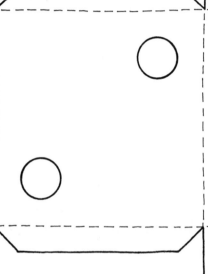

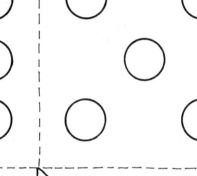

1. Cut out the die pattern on the bold line. Do not cut on the dotted lines.

2. Fold on all dotted lines and glue or tape sides to the tabs to form the die.

32   FS-10127 Logic Across the Curriculum

Name_____

Color Cube Confusion

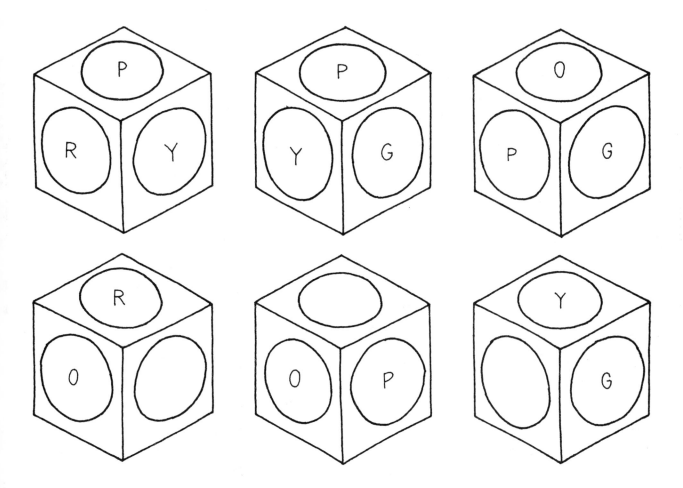

1. Color the *R* side red. Color the *B* side blue. Color the *P* side purple. Color the *O* side orange. Color the *G* side green. Color the *Y* side yellow.

2. These are six views of the same cube. Carefully study the position of the cube and then color each side of the cube with the appropriate color.

Hint: It may help if you look for a pattern and establish which colors are exactly opposite one another.

Name_____

Crazy Cube

Six different views of the same cube appear above. Color each shape a different color. Example: Color all the hearts red.

Study the pictures carefully to decide which shape belongs on the missing cube sides. Draw the appropriate shape and color it.

Name_____

Mystery Cube

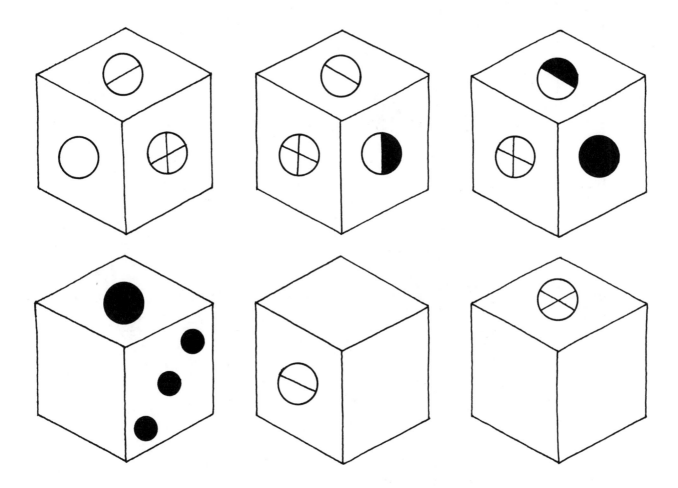

Six different views of the same cube appear above. Study each view carefully and complete the missing sides. Add color if it will help distinguish sides.

Name_____

See You at the Sockhop

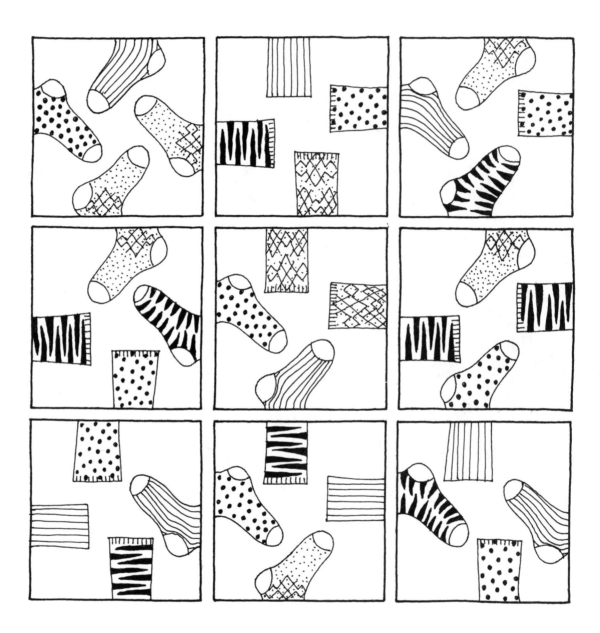

1. Identify the four different sock patterns.
2. Color socks that have the same pattern, the same color.
3. Cut out the nine squares.
4. Arrange the squares so you end up with *at least* eight complete socks.

Name_____

Mixed Veggies

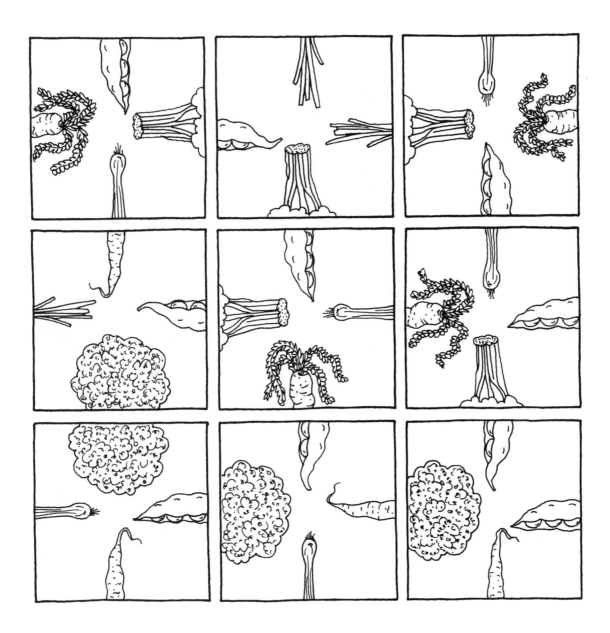

1. Identify the four different vegetables.

2. Color each veggie the appropriate color.

3. Cut out the nine squares.

4. Arrange the squares so that you have three pea pods, three broccoli stalks, three carrots, and three green onions.

Name _____

Creation Station

1. Identify the art tool patterns.

2. Color each type of art tool the same color.
   Example: Color each paintbrush blue.

3. Cut out the 9 squares.

4. Arrange the squares so that you end up with at least 12 complete art tools.

Name _____

Stop Bugging Me!

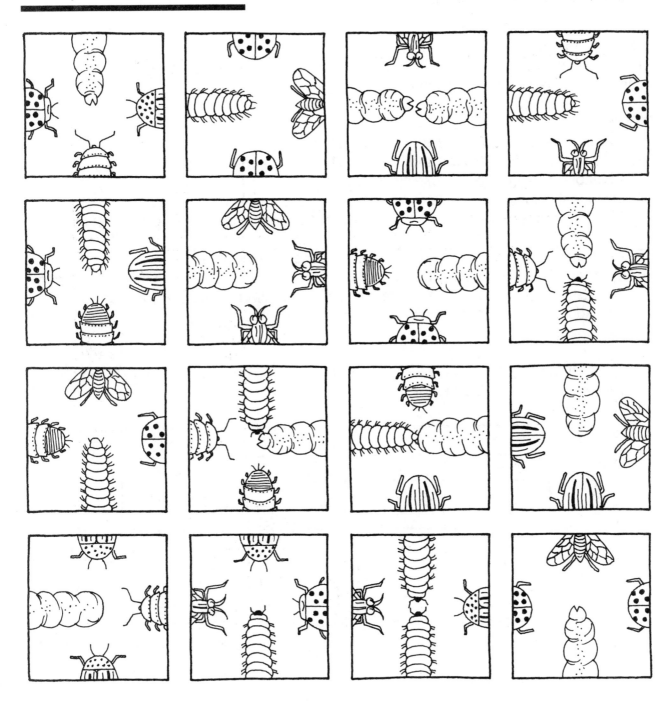

1. Identify each of the six types of bugs.

2. Color each type of bug a different color.

3. Cut out the 16 squares and arrange them. You are an expert if you can arrange it so that you have 24 bugs.

TEACHER TIDBITS — Mathematical Cross-Reference

TOPIC: Teaching students how to use a cross-reference mathematical chart to solve a logic problem.

GETTING STUDENTS MOTIVATED: Ask students how many times they have started to solve a math problem and they could not do it, even though the teacher insisted that there was enough information to solve it. Explain that they will learn to use a cross-reference math chart to help solve a logic problem.

STEPS:
1. Carefully read the introduction; then look at the chart.
2. Go back to the introduction and highlight or underline any specific information. Example: Twenty-two kids participated.
3. Write that information on the chart in the appropriate location.
4. Read the first fact. Decide if there is specific information that can be charted at this time; if so, fill it in on the chart. If not, go on to the next fact.
5. Continue this process until you have gone over each fact once.
6. Go back to the first statement and start over again, this time checking to see if you can now use the information by cross-referencing. If so, chart the new information.
7. Use addition, subtraction, and/or multiplication if needed. Example:

If you know that 11 out of the 22 are boys, then you can subtract 11 from 22 and deduce that there are also 11 girls.

	Soccer	Kickball	Tennis	Totals
Boys	4		3	11
Girls				11
Totals				22

Once you fill that in the appropriate boxes, you can cross-reference and add soccer boys (4) to the number of tennis boys (3) for a total of 7 boys so far. You now know that there are 11 boys total so you can subtract 7 from 11 to deduce that there are 4 kickball boys.

8. Continue this process until the chart is complete.

GUIDED PRACTICE: Use the following puzzle, "North to Alaska," as a class or in small-group instruction.

Name_____

North!...to Alaska!

A group of Scouts and their parents from Washington State were lucky enough to go on a week-long trip to Alaska. They were to record all the wildlife they saw. When they returned, a newspaper reporter wanted to know how many snowy owls, grizzlies, and salmon had been sighted. The group sighted 20 of these animals total. Use the chart and some logical thinking to calculate how many animals of each type were sighted.

	Snowy Owl	Grizzly	Salmon	TOTAL
Boy Scouts				
Girl Scouts				
TOTAL				

1. The same number of snowy owls was seen as were grizzlies.
   Hint: Does this fact help you at this time? If so, enter the information. If not, move on to the next one.

2. The girls did not see any salmon but the boys saw 10.
   a. Enter this information on the chart.
   b. Enter the total number of salmon sighted.
   c. You should now be able to total the number of owls and grizzlies seen.

   Still need help? Here are the facts so far: You know there were 20 animals seen. This should be written in the total column. You know how many salmon were seen, so if you add the total number of owls and grizzlies to the total number of salmon they must equal 20.
   20 - 10 salmon = _____ left (owls and bears together).
   d. Read fact #1 again. This should help you figure out the total number of owls and grizzlies. Remember the total number of owls and the total number of bears are equal. _____ + _____ = 10

3. The girls saw twice as many grizzlies as the boys saw owls.
   Ex: boys' owls x 2 = girls' grizzlies

4. The boys saw one grizzly.
   a. Look at the total number of grizzlies seen. Now calculate the number of grizzlies the girls saw.
   b. Look at clue #3 again. Complete the chart.

Blue Ridge Blossoms

Last spring Miss Petunia's class went on a hike in the Blue Ridge Mountains. Rose and Heather went crazy photographing the beautiful flowers. Use the chart, facts, and critical thinking to figure out how many photos each girl took of which flowers. There were 30 photos taken in all.

1. There were 13 photos of wild columbine and 12 taken of azaleas.
2. Heather took as many wild columbine photos as Rose's total number of pictures.
3. No photos of showy orchis were taken by Rose but she did take two more photos of azaleas than Heather took of showy orchis.

	Wild Columbine	Azaleas	Showy Orchis	TOTALS
Rose				
Heather				
TOTALS				Grand Total

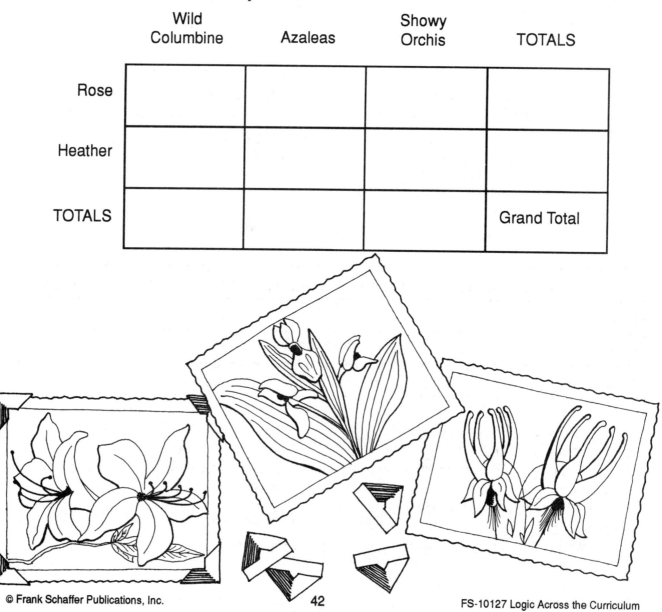

Name_____

Stormy Weather

Miss Thunder's class of 32 students became very interested in storms following one of mother nature's lightning shows over their homeland the night before. Use mathematical logic and the chart below to see how many males and females studied each type of storm.

	Tornados	Hurricanes	Thunderstorms	Blizzards	Totals
Males					
Females					
Total		12		7	32

1. The same number of males studied tornados as females studied hurricanes.
2. There were an equal number of males and females in the class.
3. If you multiply the number of males who studied blizzards by the females who studied tornados, you have the number of females who studied hurricanes.
4. Half of the males studied tornados, 12 persons total studied hurricanes, and 7 studied blizzards.
5. Three more females studied thunderstorms than males.

Name_____

Bon Voyage

At the high school in Victoria, Canada, the foreign language clubs had incredibly successful fund raisers. The students were all able to visit foreign countries for their summer class trips. Use mathematical logic to see how many students and sponsors went to each country. Ninety persons traveled.

	Mexico	France	Spain	Japan	Total
Students					
Sponsors					
Totals					

1. A total of 20 sponsors went on trips. Thirty-seven persons went to Spain.
2. If you multiply the number of students that went to Japan by the number of sponsors that went to Japan, you will know how many students went to Spain.
3. The same number of sponsors went to Mexico and France.
4. One-half as many sponsors went to France as students went to Japan.
5. Five sponsors went to Mexico and 20 persons went to France, which is twice as many students as went to Japan.

Name _____

Dance 'Til You Drop

At the Spring Festival in Battlecreek, Michigan, all fine arts students were required to perform dances. Slide through these facts and use the chart to see which dances the kids from each grade level did.

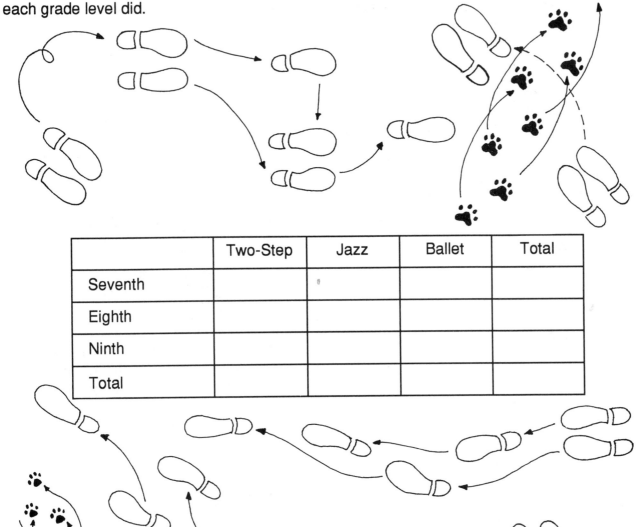

	Two-Step	Jazz	Ballet	Total
Seventh				
Eighth				
Ninth				
Total				

1. The same number of eighth and ninth graders performed jazz dance which is half the number of eighth and ninth graders who performed ballet.
2. If you add the seventh grade two-steppers to the eighth grade ballet dancers, you will have the correct number of ninth grade two-steppers.
3. Sixty kids participated and an equal number did each dance.
4. None of the seventh graders were interested in ballet but 10 performed jazz.
5. The total number of ninth graders who performed was 29.

Reduce, Re-use, Recycle

Mia, Ashley, Christina, and Gabriel were saving money for a trip to Six Flags. They decided to earn money by recycling. Use critical thinking and the chart below to calculate how many pounds of each item were recycled by each student. A total of 120 pounds was recycled.

Facts:

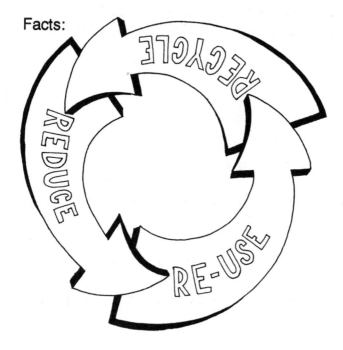

1. If you multiply Ashley's copper by Gabriel's aluminum, you know how many pounds of glass Ashley recycled.
2. Each student recycled an equal number of total pounds.
3. Christina's copper and glass are equal to the amount of her aluminum.
4. Gabriel's copper is equal to Ashley's copper times Christina's glass.
5. Mia recycled equal amounts of each item.
6. Fourty-four pounds of glass were re-cycled; Gabriel did not recycle any.
7. Ashley's copper was seven pounds less than Mia's, but Gabriel's copper was 11 pounds more than Mia's.

	Copper	Glass	Aluminum	Total
Mia				
Ashley				
Christina				
Gabriel				
Total				

　　　　　　FS-10127 Logic Across the Curriculum

Teacher Tidbits — Number Patterns

TOPIC: Teaching students how to follow a specific number sequence along with basic mathematical computation to solve a story problem.

GETTING STUDENTS MOTIVATED: Tell students to imagine that they are looking in the sky for the Big Dipper. Ask them to explain how they would know if they found it. Emphasize the fact that they would recognize it based on its pattern. Remind them that in mathematics, we often encounter many patterns also. Introduce the idea that the following activities involve solving math problems in which putting numbers in specific sequences or patterns makes solving the problems much easier.

STEPS:

1. Carefully read the introduction/directions.

2. Underline the specific question or fact that you are asked to find.

3. Take a careful look at the chart or table to see what you will need to complete or fill in to find the answer.

4. Reread the introduction and highlight any *specific* information that you can use to solve the puzzle.
   Example: Two of the 10 kids took out the trash. None of the kids were the same age as any of the others.

5. Start filling in the chart using the lowest possible numbers appropriate for that specific puzzle.
   Example: You are asked to find the ages of three teen-age brothers. The first numerical possibility is 13.

6. Continue filling in the chart using numbers in sequence. If the numbers you fill in on one line do not meet the criteria for the puzzle, use the next highest or lowest number in sequence, whichever direction is appropriate for that particular problem.

7. When you think you have found the correct answer, **GO BACK AND DOUBLE CHECK!** Make sure that your answer meets *all* the criteria given.

GUIDED PRACTICE: Use one of the following logic pages and follow these specific steps to work a specific problem as a class or in small groups. Similar problems can probably be found in a current math text.

Name_____

Patriotic Birthday

Ashley and Christina were both born on the Fourth of July! Ashley is the oldest. The sum of the girls' ages is 18 and the product is 72. Use the table below to find the ages of Ashley and Christina.

Christina's Age	Ashley's Age	Sum	Product
1	17	18	17
2	16		
3			
4			

Ashley's age _____

Christina's age _____

Name_____

Mary's Fried Okra

Mary's home-grown fried okra was the best in Hood County. She had one little problem. The goat in the area kept eating the okra before Mary could harvest it. Luckily her husband, Lou, decided to build her a fence. He bought 72 feet of fence. Use the table below to figure the length and width of the area that would give Mary the largest garden.

Length	Width	Perimeter	Area
1 foot	35 feet	72 feet	35 sq. ft.
2 feet	34 feet	72 feet	
3 feet			
4 feet			
5 feet			
	30 feet		
	29 feet		
	28 feet		

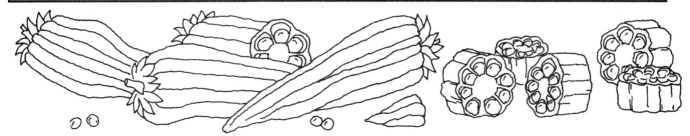

Name_____

Lucky Ducks

Pat and Helen just found out that they have inherited some money. Their Uncle Rooster, who was quite a prankster, wrote his will with a bit of a twist. He had his will written to say that the girls could have a piece of land with the perimeter 48 feet. The lot would be covered with single $1,000 bills. They could choose the dimensions of the lot. What are the length and the width of the lot that would have the biggest area, therefore giving them the most money?

Length_____ Width_____

Length	Width	Perimeter	Area
1	23	48	
2	22	48	
3			

Name_____

Kissin' Cousins

Eighteen cousins attended the Best family reunion in Little Ocmulgee Park, Georgia. If every cousin kissed all his or her cousins on the cheek, how many kisses took place? There was only one kiss exchanged between each set of cousins. Draw a chart in the space below to find how many kisses were given.

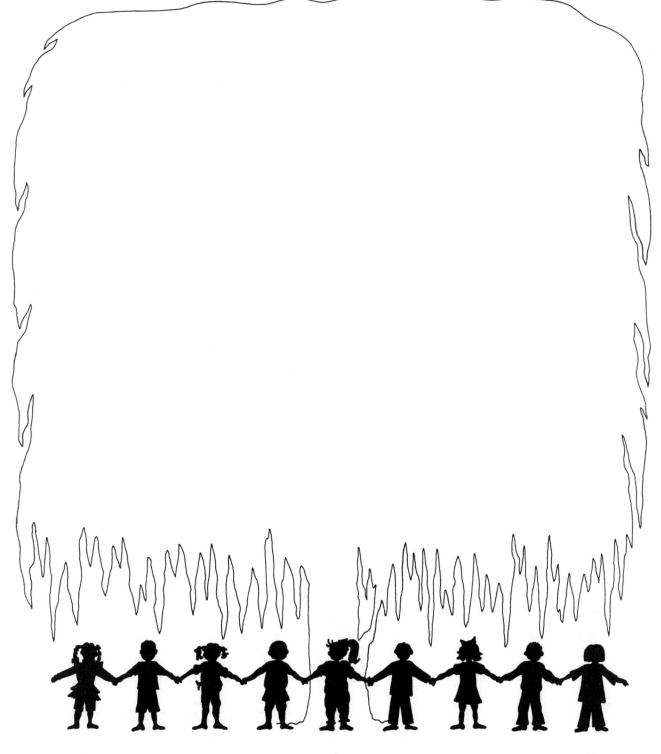

Name _____

Babysitting Bonanza

Jeremy, Waqas, Katie, and Anna went into the babysitting business together. They charged $2.00 an hour per child. They agreed to split the money equally when they worked equal amounts. Use the facts and the chart below to calculate how much each babysitter should make.

Facts:
1. The first and second hours they had 12 kids, but they had 15 for the third and fourth hours.
2. Waqas went home for lunch during the second hour.
3. Katie and Anna did not help during the fourth hour because they went to cello lessons.
4. Jeremy took a nap during the third hour.

	Hour 1 $___	Hour 2 $___	Hour 3 $___	Hour 4 $___	Total
Jeremy					
Waqas					
Katie					
Anna					

Name_____

Wild Cherries

Shannon, Brahim, and Jennifer were all excited! They met last summer at YMCA camp and were planning a reunion at the annual Cherry Festival in Traverse City, Michigan. They each had to drive a different distance and a different speed limit. Use the chart and the facts to figure out who arrived first if they all left at noon.

Facts:
Shannon:	190 miles	Speed Limit: 60 mph
Brahim:	105 miles	Speed Limit: 35 mph
Jennifer:	140 miles	Speed Limit: 50 mph

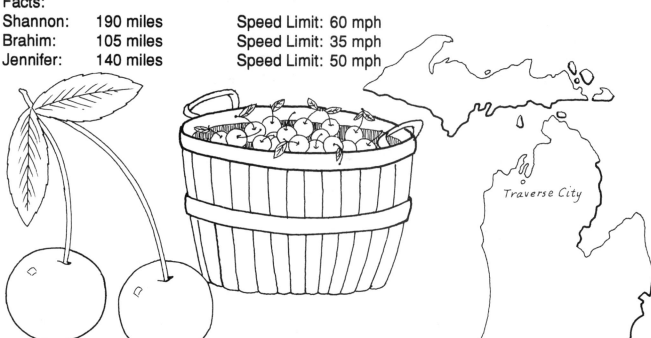

Traverse City

Travel Time	Shannon's Distance	Is She There?	Brahim's Distance	Is He There?	Jennifer's Distance	Is She There?
12:30 p.m.						
1:00 p.m.						
1:30 p.m.						
2:00 p.m.						
2:30 p.m.						
3:00 p.m.						
3:30 p.m.						

Answer: _____

Explanation: _____

Name_____

Crazy Hat Day

During School Spirit Week Mr. Tops' class members all wore their favorite kinds of hats. Use the facts to figure out how many eighth graders wore each kind of hat.

Facts:
1. An equal number of kids wore baseball hats and berets.
2. There were 1/2 as many cowboy hats as there were berets.
3. There were two more straw hats than there were sombreros.
4. There was one more sun visor than there was cowboy hats.
5. There were 1/2 as many sombreros as there were cowboy hats.
6. The number of kids who wore sombreros is the square root of four.

Baseball hats   _____   Sombreros   _____

Berets   _____   Sun visors   _____

Cowboy hats   _____   Straw hats   _____

Students   _____

Name_____

Proud Grandparents

Jean and Willis have three grandchildren named Caleb, Jacob, and Laura. Use the chart below and deductive reasoning to figure the ages of the grandchildren.

Facts:
1. Jacob is the youngest.
2. The sum of the children's ages is 11.
3. The product of their ages is 48.

Factors of 48	Product	Sum
1, 1, 48		
1, 2, 24		
1, 3, 16		
1, 4, 12		
1, 6, 8		
2, 1, 24		
2, 2, 12		
2, 3, 8		
2, 4, 6		
3, 1, 16		
3, 4, 4		
3, 6, 3		

Ages:

Jacob _____

Laura _____

Caleb _____

Ask Us About Our GRANDCHILDREN

Name_____

Rock of Ages

Jill and Sabra are exactly 25 years apart. Sabra is not a teen-ager yet. The product of the girls' ages is 396. How old is Jill?

Complete the chart to find the answer.

Sabra	Jill	Product	Answer?
1	26	26	No
2			
3			
4			
5			
6			
7			
8			
9			
10			
11			
12			

FS-10127 Logic Across the Curriculum

Name_____

Teen Challenge

Christina and Nicole are sisters. Use the chart and the listed facts to calculate each of their ages.

Facts:
1. Nicole is the youngest, Christina is a teen-ager.
2. If you multiply their ages and add 62, it will equal 300.
3. They are three years apart.

Nicole	Christina	Product	Fact #2	Answer?
10	13	10 x 13 =	+ 62 =	Yes or No
11				
12				
13				
14				
15				
16				

FS-10127 Logic Across the Curriculum

Name _____

Wrap It Up!

Cheri and Walt were selling gift wrap to raise money for their local food bank. Complete the chart and use the facts to deduce how many dollars profit they made in the first, second, and third hours.

Facts:
1. They were able to donate $11.00.
2. The product of Hour 1 x Hour 2 x Hour 3 = 36.
3. Each hour was more profitable than the last.

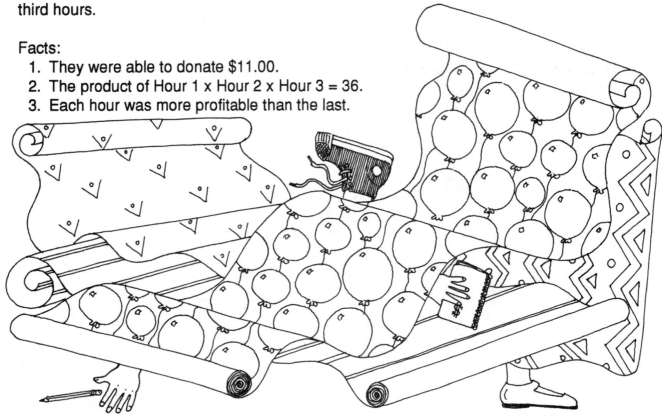

Product	Hour 1	Hour 2	Hour 3	Sum	Is this the answer?
36	1	1	36	38	No
36	1	2			
36	1				
36	1				
	1				
	2				
	2				
	2				
	3				
	3				

Name_____

A Fraction of the Cost

Last Saturday morning, five friends hit the garage sale trail. They were all looking for great deals at a fraction of the cost stores would charge. Use the statement below to figure out how much money each friend spent. Hint: Work backwards.

Statement:
Corey spent three times as much as Mary. Madeline spent 1/2 as much as Jerry. Jerry spent 1/3 as much as Corey. Ellie spent 1/5 as much as Madeline. Mary spent $20.00.

Corey $ _____

Ellie $ _____

Madeline $ _____

Jerry $ _____

Mary $ _____

Total Spent $ _____

Name_____

Mowin' Maniacs

Joseph, Gregory, Jeffrey, and Christopher went into the lawn mowing business. They charged $24.00 an acre. They mowed a total of five acres. That means they made a total of $_____. Use the facts and the chart below to figure how much money each mower should make.

Facts:
1. All the boys cut the first acre.
2. Christopher did not help with the second acre and Gregory did not help with the fourth acre.
3. Jeffrey and Christopher slept while Joseph and Gregory cut the fifth acre.
4. Christopher cut the third acre by himself.

	Acre 1	Acre 2	Acre 3	Acre 4	Acre 5	Total $
Christopher						
Gregory						
Jeffrey						
Joseph						

Teacher Tidbits—Using Conditional Statements

TOPIC: Teaching students to derive facts from conditional statements that use the following words: *and*, *if*, and *or*. This type of logical reasoning is used in the next two sections of the book, "Horizontal Elimination" and "Cross-Reference Chart Logic."

GETTING STUDENTS MOTIVATED: Tell students to imagine that their mom said they could go to the movies if they cleaned their room. Emphasize the fact that the mom said "if" meaning that there is a condition to the situation. If they do not clean their room, they do not get to go to the movies. Explain that the following logic problems use conditional statements. In other words, for one thing to be true is conditional on something else being true.

STEPS:

1. Carefully read the directions and the introduction.

2. Read each statement one at a time.

3. Go back to the first statement and read it carefully. If the statement has the word *and*, *if* or *or*, highlight or underline that specific word.

4. Read the statement again, this time in two separate parts.
   Example: Nicky grew cinnamon stick and Dallas grew mint **OR** Nicky grew mint and Walt grew sage.

5. This statement is only half true. Either the first part is true **OR** the second part is true. List one fact that the statement tells you, list more if possible.
   Example: Nicky either grew mint or cinnamon stick, he did not grow anything else. Also, mint was grown by Nicky or Dallas so Walt did not grow mint, nor did anyone else.

6. When you are solving a specific puzzle, continue this process with each statement. As soon as the skill is mastered, apply the skill to an actual logic puzzle.

GUIDED PRACTICE: To eliminate frustration and heighten students' success, use the following page, "Tossed Salad," to allow practice of the skill before applying it to a logic puzzle.

Tossed Salad

DIRECTIONS: Read each statement below one at a time. List two possible facts for each. THIS DOES NOT SOLVE A PARTICULAR PUZZLE; it simply allows you to practice the skill before you apply it to an actual problem.

EXAMPLE: Melinda brought carrots and Rose brought celery or Melinda brought red leaf lettuce and Katie brought carrots.

ANSWER: a.) Melinda brought carrots or red leaf lettuce, so she did not bring anything else.
b.) Carrots were brought by Melinda or Katie, so Rose did not bring carrots.

Now you try it!

1. If Cheri grew radishes Mike grew cucumbers but if Cheri grew cucumbers then Al grew red onions.

   a. _____

   b. _____

2. Dennis shredded cheese if Kim chopped tomatoes but Kim diced chicken if Jed shredded cheese.

   a. _____

   b. _____

3. Roger sliced zucchini if Laura chopped green onions but if Roger chopped green onions Michele washed sprouts.

   a. _____

   b. _____

4. Jean sliced mushrooms if Willis sliced bell peppers but if Willis sliced artichoke hearts, Minnie sliced mushrooms.

   a. _____

   b. _____

5. If Rob washed baby corn then Jennifer grew jicama but if Rob grew jicama then Noah chopped purple cabbage.

   a. _____

   b. _____

Teacher Tidbits — Horizontal Elimination

TOPIC: Teaching students to solve logic problems in which horizontal elimination and using conditional statements is necessary to be successful.

GETTING STUDENTS MOTIVATED: Have students imagine they are at a track meet watching different heats of the 50-yard dash for district qualifying. Tell them that in each heat, the top two sprinters go on to the semi-finals. Ask them what happens to the other runners who were not in the top two in their heats. Explain that many things in our daily lives are decided upon by the process of elimination including the type of puzzle they will learn to complete today.

STEPS:

1. Read the introduction to the logic puzzle.

2. Identify the object of the puzzle. What are you being asked?

3. Recall that horizontal is across, like the horizon.

4. Look carefully at the entire puzzle. Read all the facts/statements.

5. Notice that every possible answer is on the chart in horizontal rows.

6. Read the first statement/fact. Decide if the information is usable. If it is, decide what is not possible based on the statement. If it is not useful at this time, go on to other statements until you find something useful.

7. If you have information that allows you to eliminate a possibility, then highlight or cross out the entire horizontal row.
   Example: If a fact tells you that the mandible is not a bone in the leg, cross out every horizontal row in which the mandible and the leg match. Given the fact, none of those particular possibilities is logical.

8. Continue the process until only one horizontal line is remaining. This is the correct answer.

GUIDED PRACTICE: The puzzle "Shalom!" on the following page may be used with the whole class or in small discussion groups.

Name_____

Shalom!

In Hebrew, *Shalom* can mean different things, including "hello." Hebrew is spoken in many countries including the United States. Use deductive reasoning and the chart below to learn how the people of Germany, China, and the Netherlands greet one another.

Germany	Guten tag	China	Ni Hao	Netherlands	Goedenmorgen
Germany	Guten tag	China	Goedenmorgen	Netherlands	Ni Hao
Germany	Ni Hao	China	Guten tag	Netherlands	Goedenmorgen
Germany	Ni Hao	China	Goedenmorgen	Netherlands	Guten tag
Germany	Goedenmorgen	China	Guten tag	Netherlands	Ni Hao
Germany	Goedenmorgen	China	Ni Hao	Netherlands	Guten tag

Facts:
1. *Ni Hao* is a greeting in the Netherlands if *Goedenmorgen* is used as a greeting in Germany.
2. In China, it is not common to hear *Goedenmorgen*.
3. *Ni hao* is used in China if *Goedenmorgen* is a greeting in the Netherlands or *Guten tag* is often heard in the Netherlands if *Goedenmorgen* means "hello" in Chinese.

Mmm...Italian Ice!

Stefanie and Tabitha just cooled off with Italian ice. Stefanie's Italian ice was arancia. Use logic to solve the puzzle below and you will know what color Stefanie's ice was.

azurro	orange	giallo	yellow	arancia	blue
azurro	orange	giallo	blue	arancia	yellow
giallo	orange	azurro	yellow	arancia	blue
giallo	orange	azurro	blue	arancia	yellow
arancia	orange	giallo	yellow	azurro	blue
arancia	orange	giallo	blue	azurro	yellow

1. If azurro is orange then giallo is blue but if azurro is blue then arancia is orange.

2. If yellow is giallo then blue is azurro but if yellow is azurro then orange is giallo.

There's a Fungus Among Us

Fungi are plantlike, living things that do not contain chlorophyll. Believe it or not, you have probably eaten fungi several times.

Vince, Rayette, and Derek love fungi. Use logical reasoning and horizontal elimination to determine which type of fungi is each teen's favorite. (Yeast is what makes bread rise.)

1. If Vince loves bread then Rayette loves blue cheese, but if Rayette loves mushrooms then Derek loves blue cheese.
    Hint: Look at the clue. Which person is mentioned twice? _____ That means this person Rayette either loves _____ or _____. That means she definitely did not love _____. Eliminate every line that says she loved that.

    Look to see if a type of fungus is mentioned twice. The clue says _____ is the favorite of _____ or _____ so it is definitely not the favorite of which person? _____. Eliminate any line that says that.

2. If Derek loves blue cheese then Rayette loves bread, or if Vince loves mushrooms then Derek's favorite is bread.
    Hint: Remember these are conditional statements. It says one thing is true **OR** the other thing is true. Therefore, only half of each statement is true.

    Look at the chart. Double check the statement and see if anything is not possible based on what you have already crossed out.

    If you see something is *not* possible, cross out that part of the statement and now you know the remaining half of the clue must be true.

Rayette	blue cheese	Derek	mushrooms	Vince	yeast
Rayette	blue cheese	Derek	yeast (bread)	Vince	mushrooms
Rayette	mushrooms	Derek	blue cheese	Vince	yeast
Rayette	mushrooms	Derek	yeast	Vince	blue cheese
Rayette	yeast	Derek	mushrooms	Vince	blue cheese
Rayette	yeast	Derek	blue cheese	Vince	mushrooms

Name _____

Break the Code

Michael is trying to call his Aunt Susie in Manitoba, Canada. The trouble is, he keeps dialing the wrong area code. Use horizontal elimination to help Michael find the correct area code for Manitoba.

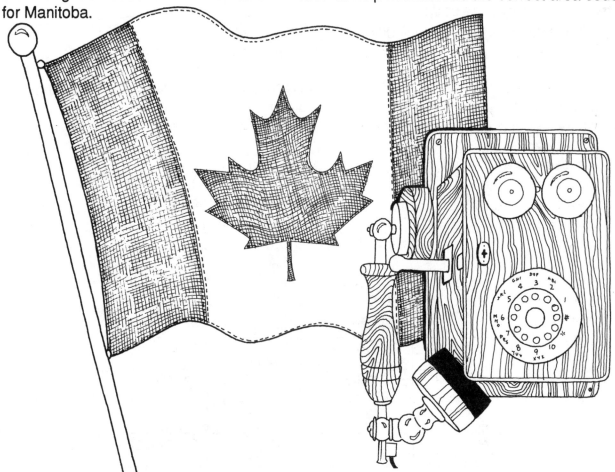

Ottawa	403	Manitoba	613	Alberta	204
Ottawa	403	Manitoba	204	Alberta	613
Ottawa	204	Manitoba	403	Alberta	613
Ottawa	204	Manitoba	613	Alberta	403
Ottawa	613	Manitoba	204	Alberta	403
Ottawa	613	Manitoba	403	Alberta	204

1. If Ottawa is 613 then Alberta is 403, but if 403 is Ottawa then Manitoba is 613.
2. If Manitoba is 613 then Ottawa is 204, but if Ottawa is 613 then Alberta is 403.

Manitoba _____   Ottawa _____   Alberta _____

Name_____

Wok 'n Roll Is Here to Stay!

Cooking in a wok and enjoying crispy eggrolls is something we have learned from another country. As a matter of fact, most of the foods we enjoy were first enjoyed in other countries. In the puzzle below, use deductive reasoning and horizontal elimination to deduce which countries first enjoyed coffee, bologna, croissants, and doughnuts.

Facts:
1. If croissants are from Ethiopia then bologna is from the Netherlands, but if croissants are from Austria then the Netherlands introduced the doughnut.
2. Coffee is from Ethiopia if bologna is from Italy, or coffee is from Austria if doughnuts are from Italy.
3. If croissants are from Italy, then coffee is from Austria.

Italy	Austria	Netherlands	Ethiopia
croissants	coffee	bologna	doughnuts
croissants	coffee	doughnuts	bologna
croissants	bologna	coffee	doughnuts
croissants	bologna	doughnuts	coffee
croissants	doughnuts	coffee	bologna
croissants	doughnuts	bologna	coffee
doughnuts	coffee	bologna	croissants
doughnuts	coffee	croissants	bologna
doughnuts	bologna	coffee	croissants
doughnuts	bologna	croissants	coffee
doughnuts	croissants	coffee	bologna
doughnuts	croissants	bologna	coffee
bologna	croissants	doughnuts	coffee
bologna	croissants	coffee	doughnuts
bologna	coffee	croissants	doughnuts
bologna	coffee	doughnuts	croissants
bologna	doughnuts	coffee	croissants
bologna	doughnuts	croissants	coffee
coffee	doughnuts	bologna	croissants
coffee	doughnuts	croissants	bologna
coffee	croissants	doughnuts	bologna
coffee	croissants	bologna	doughnuts
coffee	bologna	croissants	doughnuts
coffee	bologna	doughnuts	croissants

Italy _____ Austria _____ Netherlands _____ Ethiopia _____

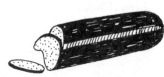

Name_____

Bonjour Étudiantes

"Bonjour Étudiantes" is what Michele saw on the chalkboard as she entered her first French class. Being a native of Quebec, Canada, she felt it was her duty to learn French. Use horizontal elimination to match these French translations to *watch, pen, book*, and *wall* to see what Michele learned the first day.

Facts:
1. If un stylo is a watch then un livre is a wall, but if a watch is une montre then un stylo is a pen.
2. Un mur is a wall.

Watch _____   Pen _____   Book _____   Wall _____

Watch	Pen	Book	Wall
une montre	un mur	un stylo	un livre
une montre	un mur	un livre	un stylo
une montre	un livre	un mur	un stylo
une montre	un livre	un stylo	un mur
une montre	un stylo	un mur	un livre
une montre	un stylo	un livre	un mur
un stylo	une montre	un mur	un livre
un stylo	une montre	un livre	un mur
un stylo	un livre	un mur	une montre
un stylo	un livre	une montre	un mur
un stylo	un mur	un livre	une montre
un stylo	un mur	une montre	un livre
un mur	un stylo	un livre	une montre
un mur	un stylo	une montre	un livre
un mur	une montre	un stylo	un livre
un mur	une montre	un livre	un stylo
un mur	un livre	un stylo	une montre
un mur	un livre	une montre	un stylo
un livre	une montre	un stylo	un mur
un livre	une montre	un mur	un stylo
un livre	un stylo	une montre	un mur
un livre	un stylo	un mur	une montre
un livre	un mur	un stylo	une montre
un livre	un mur	une montre	un stylo

Teacher Tidbits — Cross-Reference Chart Logic

TOPIC: Teaching students to deduce facts from conditional statements and organize them on a cross-reference chart.

GETTING MOTIVATED: Ask students to think back to when they have plotted points on a coordinate graph. Remind them that they usually find a number horizontally then they find a number vertically and plot the point where the two would meet if there were an imaginary line drawn. Explain that cross-reference chart logic is similar to coordinate graphing except that it uses cross-references with the process of elimination.

STEPS:

1. Carefully read the introduction.
2. Review the directions of horizontal and vertical.
3. Look at the horizontal information given; then look at the vertical information given. Identify a specific example of a cross-reference on the chart.
4. Read the first statement and establish a fact if possible.
   Example: *Hola* is Spanish if *bon jour* is French, or *bon jour* is Spanish and the French word is *arigato*. Facts: *Bon jour* is French or Spanish. The French word is *arigato* or *bon jour.*
5. Chart the facts that you have learned.
   Example: If *bon jour* is French or Spanish, you can find *bon jour* on the chart and eliminate all other languages except for French and Spanish. Do this by placing *Xs* in those specific boxes. The *bon jour*/French box and the *bon jour*/Spanish box should remain open at this time.
6. Continue this process. When you have eliminated everything except one box either horizontally or vertically, this is the answer for that particular cross-reference. Place a "yes" in that box. Take a look at the possibilities that the new fact now eliminates and place an *X* in each of those boxes.
7. When you have read through all the facts and charted the information, go back to number 1 and read it again.
8. Looking at the two separate parts, examine the first half of the statement; then look at the chart to see if that is still a possibility or if it has been eliminated. Repeat with the second part of the statement.
9. If you decide that one-half of the statement is not possible, draw a line through the entire statement that is not true. This means that the other part of the statement must be true.
10. This should free up new information. Chart it using the same process as before.
11. Continue this process until the problem is solved.

GUIDED PRACTICE: Complete the following puzzle, "The Gang's All Here," while giving step-by-step instructions. Use specific examples from the actual puzzle. Have fun!

Name_____

The Gang's All Here!

Yousef and Billy were surprised to discover that a group or gang of fish is called a school of fish. This made them interested to do some research in the library to find out what other groups of animals are called. Use deductive reasoning and the chart below to find out what Yousef and Billy learned.

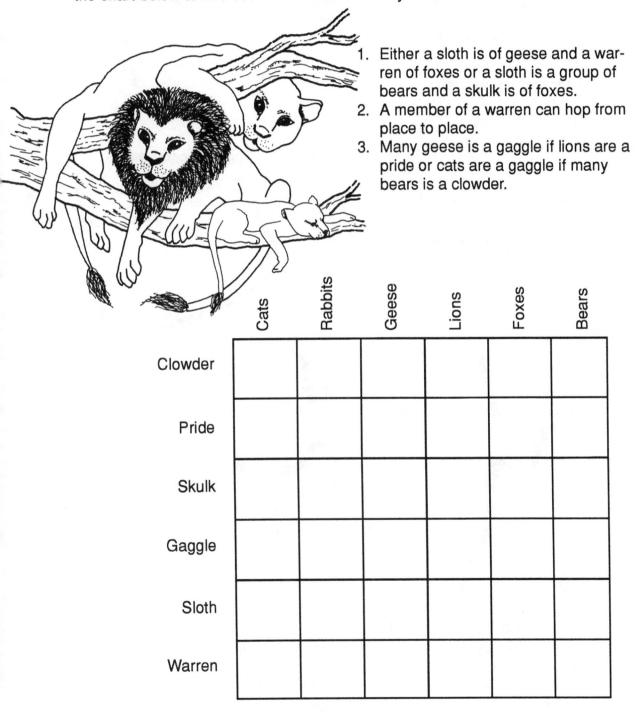

1. Either a sloth is of geese and a warren of foxes or a sloth is a group of bears and a skulk is of foxes.
2. A member of a warren can hop from place to place.
3. Many geese is a gaggle if lions are a pride or cats are a gaggle if many bears is a clowder.

	Cats	Rabbits	Geese	Lions	Foxes	Bears
Clowder						
Pride						
Skulk						
Gaggle						
Sloth						
Warren						

Name_____

The Ballot Box

Do you know the name of the basketball team at the Electoral College? Good! You should not because it is not a school! The Electoral College is the name for electors who choose the president and vice-president of the United States. Each state gets the number of votes that is equal to its senators and congressional representatives. In the puzzle below, you will use deductive reasoning to find out how many electoral votes each of the six largest states gets.

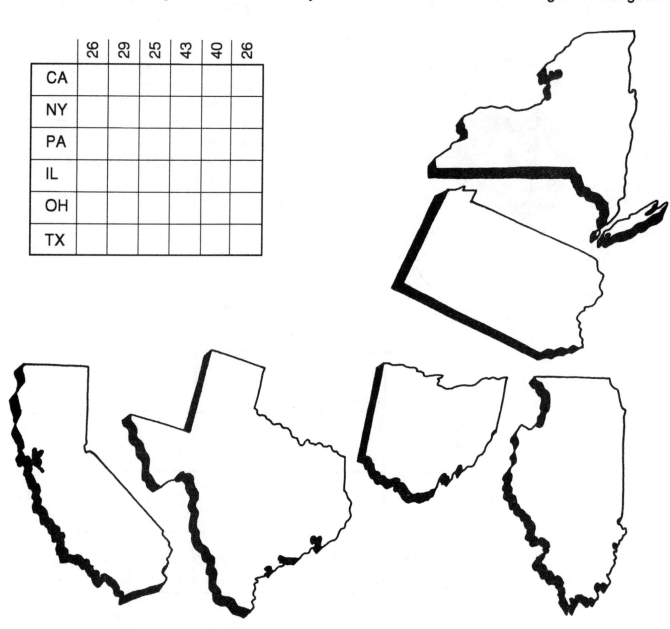

	26	29	25	43	40	26
CA						
NY						
PA						
IL						
OH						
TX						

1. Pennsylvania has less than California.
2. Either New York has the most and Texas has the lowest number listed, or New York has the least and Texas has 26.
3. If Pennsylvania has 43 then Ohio has 40, but if Ohio has 26 then 43 is New York.
4. Illinois and Ohio have the same amount of electoral votes.

Name_____

Wow! Did You Know...?

Kendelle and Dillon were giving a presentation in front of their class. They had planned to discuss baby animals, but during their research they came across some really unusual animal facts and decided to do the report on these wild findings. Dig through the conditional statements and match each animal with an amazing animal fact.

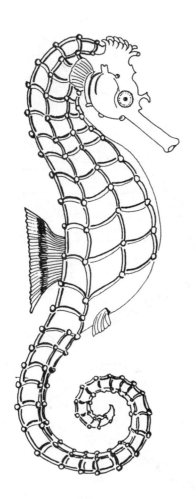

	Male gets pregnant	Female eats mate	Cannot move backwards	Mammal that lays eggs	Has male and female organs	Male nests egg on his "feet"
Nudibranch						
King Penguin						
Praying Mantis						
Kangaroo						
Seahorse						
Duckbill Platypus						

1. Either the praying mantis has both sex organs and the duckbill platypus cannot go backwards or the praying mantis eats her mate and the nudibranch has both sex organs.

2. If the seahorse male gets pregnant then the mammal that lays eggs is a duckbill platypus or the king penguin has both male and female organs and the platypus male gets pregnant.

3. The kangaroo does not lay eggs.

Name_____

Claim to Fame

Following Columbus' voyage in 1492, many French and English explorers continued to sail looking for a Northwest Passage to Asia. They believed there was a waterway through North America that linked the Pacific and Atlantic oceans. Although they were unsuccessful, they claimed many new lands for France and England and changed history forever. Use logic to match the explorers below with their "claims to fame."

	Explored the Atlantic Coast	Claimed Newfoundland	Explored Mississippi River Valley	Established French Colonies	Claimed St. Lawrence River Valley	Claimed Hudson River Valley	Established Virginia
Marquette and Joliet							
Henry Hudson							
Samuel de Champlain							
Sir Walter Raleigh							
Jacques Cartier							
Giovanni de Verrazano							
John Cabot							

1. Either Marquette and Joliet explored the Mississippi and Raleigh established Virginia, or Raleigh explored the Mississippi and Jacques Cartier established Virginia.
2. If Cabot claimed the Hudson River Valley then Raleigh claimed Newfoundland, but if Cabot claimed Newfoundland then the Hudson River was claimed by Henry Hudson.
3. Verrazano explored the Atlantic coast if Champlain established French colonies, but if Verrazano claimed Newfoundland then Cabot explored the Atlantic coast.
4. Raleigh did not explore the Mississippi River Valley.

Name_____

Aloha!

That's what Teresa, Wally, and Tiffany heard as they deboarded the plane in Maui, Hawaii. They were also given flower leis, or wreaths, to match these other English words with a word that is used in Hawaii.

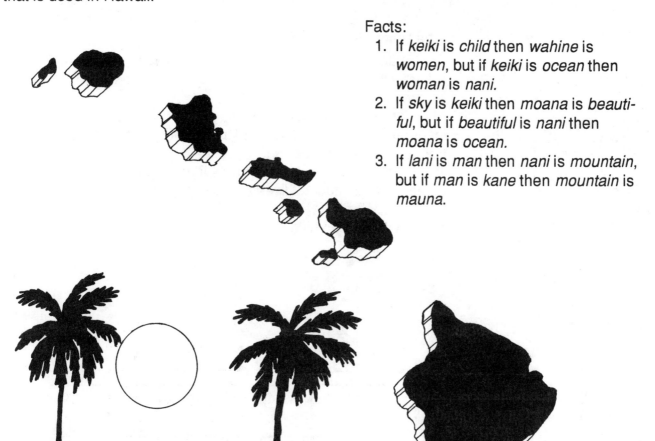

Facts:
1. If *keiki* is *child* then *wahine* is *women*, but if *keiki* is *ocean* then *woman* is *nani*.
2. If *sky* is *keiki* then *moana* is *beautiful*, but if *beautiful* is *nani* then *moana* is *ocean*.
3. If *lani* is *man* then *nani* is *mountain*, but if *man* is *kane* then *mountain* is *mauna*.

	Mountain	Sky	Woman	Man	Ocean	Beautiful	Child
Mauna							
Moana							
Nani							
Wahine							
Lani							
Kane							
Keiki							

Name_____

Home Sweet Home

When you were younger you may have thought that all native Americans lived in tepees. Now that you are maturing as a learner, you probably realize that the use of tepees was not logical for every single tribe. Dance around with these statements and use deductive reasoning to discover in what types of housing certain tribes of native Americans lived. If you have extra time, look up some more facts to see in which parts of the United States these native Americans lived.

1. The Apache lived in the longhouse if the Navajo lived in adobe villages or the Kickapoo lived in wigwams if the Apache lived in brush lodges.
2. The Navajo lived in hogans while the Iroquois lived in the longhouses or the Pueblo lived in the wigwams and the Iroquois lived in the hogans.
3. The Seminoles lived in thatch huts if the Sioux lived in tepees or the Apaches lived in wigwams and the Navajo lived in tepees.
4. The Navajo did not live in adobe villages.

	Kickapoo	Pueblo	Sioux	Apache	Navajo	Iroquois	Seminoles
Buffalo Hide Tepee							
Hogan							
Wigwam							
Longhouse							
Brush Lodge							
Adobe Village							
Thatch Hut							

Name_____

Merry Christmas From Around the World

If someone walked up to you and said, "Boldog Karacsony Unnep," he or she would be saying "Merry Christmas" in Dutch. Solve the puzzle below and learn how to say "Merry Christmas" in nine more countries.

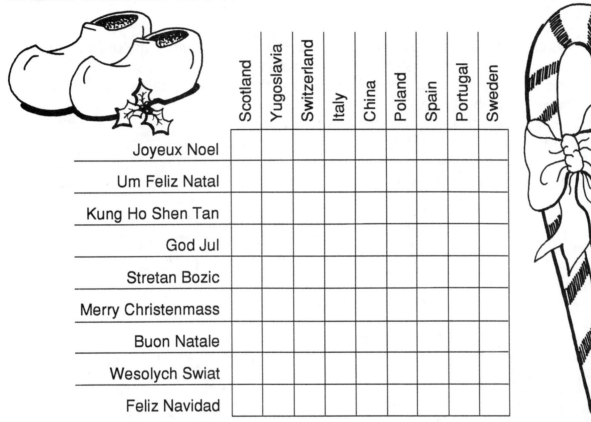

	Scotland	Yugoslavia	Switzerland	Italy	China	Poland	Spain	Portugal	Sweden
Joyeux Noel									
Um Feliz Natal									
Kung Ho Shen Tan									
God Jul									
Stretan Bozic									
Merry Christenmass									
Buon Natale									
Wesolych Swiat									
Feliz Navidad									

1. If *God Jul* is from Sweden, then *Buon Natale* is Italian or *God Jul* is from Poland and *Kung Ho Shen Tan* is Swedish.

2. In Switzerland they say *Merry Christenmass* if they say *Stretan Bozic* in China or they say *Kung Ho Shen Tan* in China and *Merry Christenmass* in Scotland.

3. *Wesolych Swiat* is spoken in Yugoslavia if *Joyeux Noel* is spoken in Spain or *Wesolych Swiat* is the greeting in Poland and *Joyeux Noel* is used in Switzerland.

4. If the Swedish phrase is *Stretan Bozic* then the Scottish phrase is *Joyeux Noel* but if *Kung Ho Shen Tan* is Chinese then the Swedish phrase is *God Jul.*

5. *Um Feliz Natal* is spoken in Portugal if *Joyeux Noel* is said in Switzerland or *Um Feliz Natal* is spoken in Spain and *Feliz Navidad* is Italian.

6. *Stretan Bozic* is not Spanish.

Name_____

Now That's Big!

Linda and Sarah decided to take a meter stick and measure off the length of some dinosaurs just to see how big they actually were. The girls were amazed! Read the conditional statements below and solve the puzzle to find the approximate average length of nine prehistoric animals.

1. If the Tyrannosaurus was five meters then the Protoceratops was 7 meters, but if the Tyrannosaurus was 15 meters then the Ankylosaurus was 7.
2. If you add the length of the Dimetrodon to the length of the Triceratops, then you will have the length of the Trachodon.
3. The Stegosaurus was longer than the Styracosaurus.
4. The longest dinosaur on the chart is the Diplodocus if the shortest is the Protoceratops, but if the longest is the Tyrannosaurus then the shortest is the Stegosaurus.
5. If the Trachodon was 13 meters then the Triceratops was 10, but if the Protoceratops was 13 then the Stegosaurus was 5.

	2 Meters	3 Meters	5 Meters	6 Meters	7 Meters	10 Meters	13 Meters	15 Meters	29 Meters
Triceratops									
Trachodon									
Tyrannosaurus									
Stegosaurus									
Dimetrodon									
Protoceratops									
Diplodocus									
Styracosaurus									
Ankylosaurus									

May I Borrow a Cup of Sugar, Please?

It seems like every time Melisa turned around, her neighbor Bonnie was knocking on the door asking to borrow something. Bonnie was afraid that she was beginning to bother Melisa, but Melisa explained that people have been "borrowers" forever. She even told Bonnie words that Americans have borrowed from other languages. Borrow some facts from the statements below and match each borrowed word with the corresponding language.

1. *Coleslaw* is French if *piano* is Yiddish or *piano* is Italian and *souvenir* is French.
2. The Malay word is *ketchup* if the Hindi word is *shampoo* or the Arabic word is *ketchup* and the Hindi word is *squash*.
3. Either *kosher* is Yiddish and *smorgasbord* is Scandinavian or the Yiddish word is *smorgasbord* and the Scandinavian word is *kindergarten*.
4. If *alcohol* is Dutch then *coleslaw* is German but if *coleslaw* is Dutch then *squash* is native American.
5. The Hindi word is *piano* and the native American word is *shampoo* or the Hindi word is *shampoo* and *kosher* is Yiddish.
6. *Kindergarten* is German if *smorgasbord* is Scandinavian or *alcohol* is native American if *coleslaw* is French.

	Yiddish	German	Malay	Scandinavian	Dutch	Native American	Italian	Hindi	French	Arabic
Shampoo										
Ketchup										
Alcohol										
Kindergarten										
Souvenir										
Coleslaw										
Squash										
Piano										
Kosher										
Smorgasbord										

Teacher Tidbits — Language Arts Brain Teasers

TOPIC: This page of Teacher Tidbits varies from the previous ones in that it does not explain the teaching steps of one particular type of logical or deductive process. The following section is a small collection of brain teasers that encourages flexibility in thinking and thus involves no particular defined thinking process. The paragraphs below will give a brief overview of each specific puzzle.

You Are My Sunshine: This is a fun exploration of idioms that we commonly use in the English language. It is intended to be a good introduction to a lesson on communication. It can also be taken further and turned into an art lesson.

Dress the Turkey: Use the same procedure as with "You Are My Sunshine."

Get It Together: This is a real thinking activity. The two most important things to stress are #1: The missing word may precede or follow the words already given, or it may precede some and follow others within the same row; #2: Some may be actual compound words while others may simply be words that are commonly used together. This is an excellent group activity.

Two Peas in a Pod: This puzzle simply encourages flexibility in thinking. Encourage the students to examine every possibility. This is not intended to be an independent activity due to the high frustration it may cause. Remind students to go through and write in the ones they think they know first and go back to the ones they view as more difficult.

Eight Legs on a Spider: Same procedure as "Two Peas in a Pod."

FINAL NOTE: These are supposed to be fun! They are great for small contests, especially on rainy days.

You Are My Sunshine!

Imagine your grandma squeezing you tight, pinching your cheeks, kissing you all over your face and saying, "Oh, you are my sunshine." Does your grandma really think you are a ball of fire in the sky? No, Of course not! She is using an idiomatic expression. That is an expression, sentence, or phrase that does not literally mean what is being said. Idiomatic expressions are used in all languages. For this activity you need to really "stretch your brain." Study the pictures below and see if you can write the idiomatic expression to which each picture refers. Well, get busy! "Hop to it!"

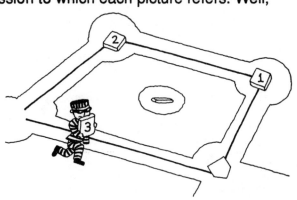

_____

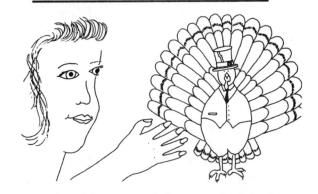

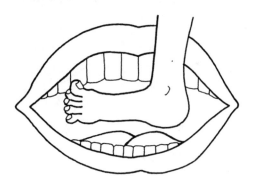

_____

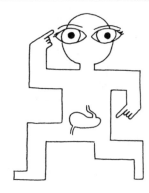

_____

Name_____

Dress the Turkey

Remember last Thanksgiving when your mom, grandma, or Aunt Clara said "Well, I better go dress the turkey"? She used an idiomatic expression. She really did not put clothes on the turkey, at least we hope not! Below, you will find nine boxes. In the boxes that have a picture try to figure out to which idiom it refers. Write the idiom on the line provided. In each of the boxes in which an idiom appears, illustrate it in a creative way. Zip your lip and tackle the problems!

You're pulling my leg.

You are the apple of my eye

My room is a pig pen.

I'll be a monkey's uncle.

Name_____

Get It Together

In English we often combine two words to make a new word. In the list below you will find rows of three words. Each of the words can be joined with another word either before or after it to make three new words. The first one is completed for you. Your task is to think of the fourth word which can be paired up with the other three to make three new words.

1.	sled	tail	cat	<u>bob</u>
2.	storm	wash	less	_____
3.	dog	doze	pen	_____
4.	saw	smoker	link	_____
5.	up	point	out	_____
6.	birth	labor	hood	_____
7.	diamond	piggy	pack	_____
8.	juke	office	kite	_____
9.	syrup	meal	starch	_____
10.	father	jury	child	_____
11.	chest	dry	cube	_____
12.	knife	rabbit	pot	_____
13.	jay	board	cross	_____
14.	suit	ball	long	_____
15.	worm	end	mark	_____

Name _____

Two Peas in a Pod

It seems like we are surrounded by numbers. We encounter them many times each day and are familiar with the specific numbers of many things, (such as 26 letters in the alphabet). In the puzzle below you will have a number and a letter clue to figure out which phrase is appropriate for that specific number. Some are very difficult while others are quite easy. They are not listed in any specific order, so it might help to go through and complete the ones that you can do easily first. Good luck and have fun!

1. 2 P in a P   2 Peas in a Pod _____
2. 360 D in a C   _____
3. 206 B in the B   _____
4. 10 D in a D   _____
5. 12 E in a D   _____
6. 7 C on the E   _____
7. 2 S to every S   _____
8. 4 C in a S   _____
9. 4 C of the H   _____
10. 9 L of the C   _____
11. 144 I in a S F   _____
12. 2,000 P in a T   _____
13. 0 C in W   _____
14. 9 S by a S I T   _____
15. 7 D in a P N   _____
16. 4 S in a Q   _____
17. 5 C in a P H   _____
18. 8 A on an O   _____
19. 8 S on a S S   _____
20. 3 W on a T   _____

Name_____

Eight Legs on a Spider

Numbers, numbers, numbers...it seems like we cannot even go through an hour's time without dealing with numbers in some way. In the puzzle below you will have a number and a letter clue to help you figure out a particular phrase that uses a specific number. They are not listed in any specific order, so it is easiest to look for the most obvious ones before tackling the difficult. Have fun!

1.   8 L on a S   _____

2.   32 O in a Q   _____

3.   100 P in a D   _____

4.   3 S and Y O   _____

5.   12 M in a Y   _____

6.   3 LP   _____

7.   3 S on a T   _____

8.   9 I in a B B G (without E I)   _____

9.   180 D in a S L   _____

10.   1 A a D K the D A   _____

11.   7 D Y to every H Y   _____

12.   50 S on the A F   _____

13.   4 Q in a G   _____

14.   50 or 100 Y in a D   _____

15.   8 M a M   _____

16.   100 Y on a FB F   _____

17.   4 P on M R   _____

18.   5 C B   _____

19.   4 M F G   _____

20.   9 M of P   _____

Answer Key

Yo Tengo Hambre (page 5)
1. El queso is cheese.
2. El pollo is chicken.
3. La manzana is apple.
4. El tocino is bacon.

This Is the Life (page 6)
Jaguar - 14 years
Zebra - 22 years
Hippopotamus - 40 years

Funny Bones (page 7)
Shin - tibia
Collarbone - clavicle
Kneecap - patella
Shoulder blade - scapula

You Must Have Been a Beautiful Baby (page 8)
Kangaroo - joey
Turkey - poult
Goat - kid
Swan - cygnet
Beaver - kit

America or Bust! (page 9)
Irish, 1 1/2 million, potato crop failure
Italians, 4 1/2 million, poverty and overpopulation
Jews, 2 1/2 million, religious persecution

Let's Communicate (page 10)
John Bardeen, Transistor, 1948
Samuel Morse, Telegraph, 1840
George Eastman, Polaroid Camera, 1948
Thomas Edison, Phonograph, 1877
Alexander Grahm Bell, Telephone, 1876

Elementary, My Dear Watson! (page 11)
Cu, Copper, #29
Ag, Silver, #47
Na, Sodium, #11
Fe, Iron, #26
Hg, Mercury, #80
Au, Gold, #79

Thanks for the Gumball, Mickey! (page 12)
Dutch, Dank, Ja
Japanese, Arigato, Hai
Swahili, Asante, Noio
Hebrew, Todah, Kane
Portuguese, Obrigado, Sim
Polish, Dziekije, Tak
Russian, Spasibo, Da
German, Danke Schon, Ja

Gentlemen, Start Your Engines! (page 13)
James Watt, Scottish, Steam Engine, 1760
John Fitch, American, Steamboat, 1787
Richard Trevithick, English, Steam Locomotive, 1804

Capital Punishment (page 14)
Montana, Helena, Treasure State, 1889
Louisiana, Baton Rouge, Pelican State, 1812
West Virginia, Charleston, Mountain State, 1863
North Dakota, Bismarck, Flickertail State, 1889

All In Favor Say "I" (page 15)
Indiana, cardinal, tulip, peony, home of Raggedy Ann
Illinois, cardinal, violet, white oak, first metal framed
    skyscraper.
Iowa, goldfinch, wild rose, oak, shortest railroad
Idaho, bluebird, syringa, white pine, crystal ice cave

How's the Weather? (page 16)
Jackson, Mississippi, Summer-92, Winter-60, P-15"
Duluth, Minnesota, Summer-73, Winter-21, P-8"
Juneau, Alaska, Summer-63, Winter-31, P-17"
Lincoln, Nebraska, Summer-86, Winter-36, P-8"

Say Aaahhh! (page 18)

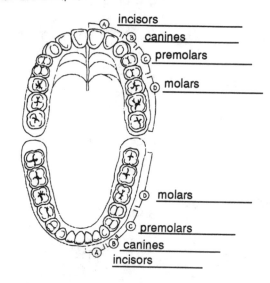

That's a Lot of Water! (page 19)
Chang - 3800
Amazon - 4000
Mississippi - 3500
Nile - 4300

Where in the World? (page 20)

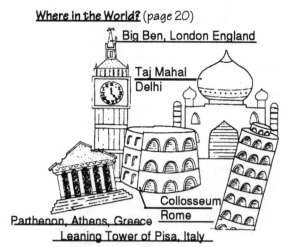

Big Ben, London England

Taj Mahal
Delhi

Collosseum
Rome

Parthenon, Athens, Greece

Leaning Tower of Pisa, Italy

Mom, I'm Movin' Out! (page 21)

Bobcat - 10 months
Deer - 12 months
Seal - 12 months
Bear - 24 months
Elephant - 44 months

Flying High (page 22)

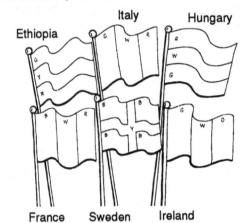

Ethiopia

Italy

Hungary

France

Sweden

Ireland

Flex It! (page 23)

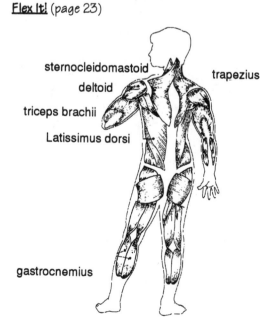

sternocleidomastoid

trapezius

deltoid

triceps brachii

Latissimus dorsi

gastrocnemius

Ouch! (page 24)

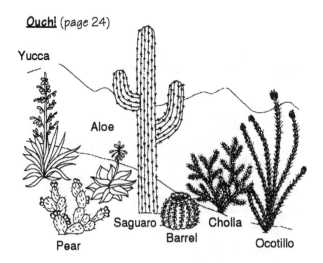

Yucca

Aloe

Saguaro

Cholla

Ocotillo

Pear

Barrel

Clickety Clack (page 25)

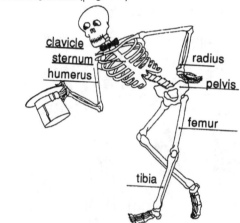

clavicle
sternum
humerus

radius

pelvis

femur

tibia

¡Viva la Conquistadores! (page 26)

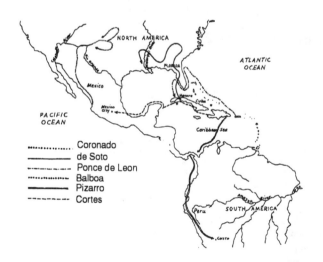

Coronado
de Soto
Ponce de Leon
Balboa
Pizarro
Cortes

Stars and Stripes Forever (page 27)

Relax, There's Plenty of Time (page 28)

Space Cowboy (page 29)

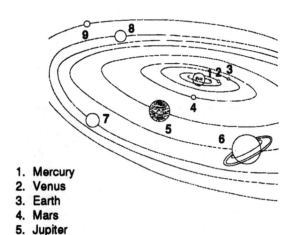

1. Mercury
2. Venus
3. Earth
4. Mars
5. Jupiter
6. Saturn
7. Uranus
8. Neptune
9. Pluto

Chess Stress (page 30)

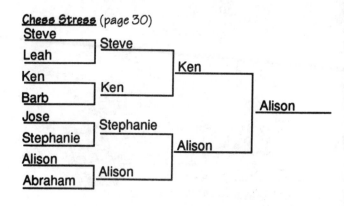

* This is one possible solution but not the only specific one. The important thin is that the players have the opponents of each game correct.

Color Cube Confusion (page 33)

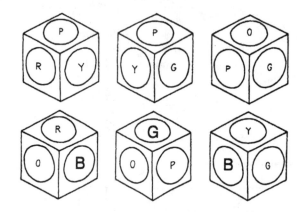

Crazy Cube (page 34)

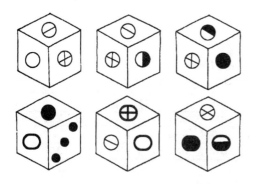

Mystery Cube (page 35)

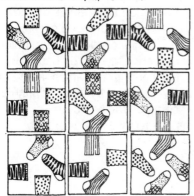

See You at the Sockhop (page 36)

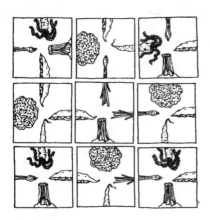

Mixed Veggies (page 37)

Creation Station (page 38)

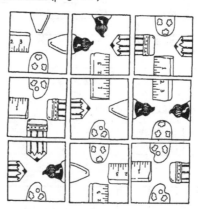

Stop Bugging Me! (page 39)

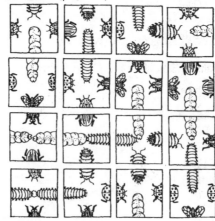

North!...to Alaska! (page 41)

	Snowy Owl	Grizzly	Salmon	TOTAL
Boy Scouts	2	1	10	13
Girl Scouts	3	4	0	17
TOTAL	5	5	10	20

Blue Ridge Blossoms (page 42)

	Wild Columbine	Azaleas	Showy Orchis	TOTALS
Rose	3	7	0	10
Heather	10	5	5	20
TOTALS	13	12	5	30

Stormy Weather (page 43)

	Tornado	Hurricane	Thunderstorm	Blizzard	Totals
Males	8	4	0	4	16
Females	2	8	3	3	16
Total	10	12	8	7	32

Bon Voyage (page 44)

	Mexico	France	Spain	Japan	Total
Students	15	15	30	10	70
Sponsors	5	5	7	3	20
Totals	20	20	37	13	90

Dance 'Til You Drop (page 45)

	2-Step	Jazz	Ballet	Total
Seventh	4	10	0	14
Eighth	2	5	10	17
Ninth	14	5	10	29
Total	20	20	20	60

Reduce, Reuse, Recycle (page 46)

	Copper	Glass	Aluminum	Totals
Mia	10	10	10	30
Ashley	3	27	0	30
Christina	8	7	15	30
Gabriel	21	0	9	30
Total	42	44	34	120

Patriotic Birthday (page 48)

Ashley's age - 12
Christina's age - 6

Mary's Fried Okra (page 49)

18' x 18'

Lucky Ducks (page 50)

Length - 12
Width - 12

Kissin' Cousins (page 51)

153 Kisses

Babysitting Bonanza (page 52)

Hour	1 = $24	2 = $24	3 = $30	4 = $30	Total = $108
Jeremy	6	8	00	15	29
Waqas	6	0	10	15	31
Katie	6	8	10	0	24
Anna	6	8	10	0	24

Wild Cherries (page 53)

Even though Jennifer and Brahim both arrived by 3:00 p.m., Jennifer could have driven 150 miles by this time. She only had to drive 140 miles so she actually would have arrived a little before 3:00 p.m. Brahim had to drive exactly 105 miles which would have taken him until 3:00 p.m. exactly.

Crazy Hat Day (page 54)

Baseball hats	8	Sombreros	2
Berets	8	Sun visors	5
Cowboy hats	4	Students	31
Straw	4		

Proud Grandparents (page 55)

Jacob - 3
Laura - 4
Caleb - 4

Rock of Ages (page 56)

Sabra is 11 and Jill is 36.

Teen Challenge (page 57)

Nicole is 14 and Christina is 17.

Wrap It Up! (page 58)

Hour 1 - $2
Hour 2 - $3
Hour 3 - $6

A Fraction of the Cost (page 59)

Corey	$ 60
Ellie	$ 2
Madeline	$ 10
Jerry	$ 20
Mary	$ 20
Total Spent	$112

Mowin' Maniacs (page 60)

	Acre1	Acre 2	Acre 3	Acre 4	Acre 5	Total $
Christopher	$6.00	0	24.00	8.00	0	$38.00
Gregory	$6.00	8.00	0	0	12.00	$26.00
Jeffrey	$6.00	8.00	0	8.00	0	$22.00
Joseph	$6.00	8.00	0	8.00	12.00	$34.00

Tossed Salad (page 62)

1. Cheri grew radishes or cucumbers.
   Cucumbers were grown by Mike or Cheri.
2. Cheese was shredded by Dennis or Jed.
   Kim chopped tomatoes or diced chicken.
3. Roger sliced zucchini or sliced green onions.
   Green onions were chopped by Laura or Roger.
4. Willis sliced bell peppers or artichoke hearts.
   Mushrooms were sliced by Jean or Minnie.
5. Rob grew jicama or washed corn.
   Jicama was grown by Jennifer or Rob.

Shalom! (page 64)

Germany - Guten Tag
China - Ni Hao
Netherlands - Goedenmorgen

Mmm...Italian Ice! (page 65)

arancia	orange	giallo	yellow	azurro	blue

There's a Fungus Among Us (page 66)

Rayette	blue cheese
Derek	yeast (bread)
Vince	mushrooms

Break the Code (page 67)

Ottawa - 613
Manitoba - 204
Alberta - 403

Wok 'n Roll Is Here to Stay! (page 68)

Italy - bologna
Austria - croissants
Netherlands - doughnuts
Ethiopia - coffee

Bonjour Étudiantes (page 69)

Watch - une montre
Pen - un stylo
Wall - un mur
Book - un livre

The Gang's All Here! (page 71)

	Cats	Rabbits	Geese	Lions	Foxes	Bears
Clowder	Yes	X	X	X	X	X
Pride	X	X	X	Yes	X	X
Skulk	X	X	X	X	Yes	X
Gaggle	X	X	Yes	X	X	X
Sloth	X	X	X	X	X	Yes
Warren	X	Yes	X	X	X	X

The Ballot Box (page 72)

CA - 40
NY - 43
PA - 29
IL - 26
OH - 26
TX - 25

Wow! Did You Know…? (page 73)

Nudibranchs: Has male and female organs
King Penguin: Male nests egg on his "feet"
Praying Mantis: Female eats mate
Kangaroo: Cannot move backwards
Seahorse: Male gets pregnant
Duckbill Platypus: Mammal that lays eggs

Claim to Fame (page 74)

Marquette and Joliet - Explored Mississippi River
     Valley
Henry Hudson - Claimed Hudson River Valley
Samuel de Champlain - Established French Colonies
Sir Walter Raleigh - Established Virginia
Jacques Cartier - Claimed St. Lawrence River Valley
Giovanni de Verrazano - Explored Atlantic Coast
John Cabot - Claimed Newfoundland

Aloha! (page 75)

Mauna - Mountain
Moana - Ocean
Nani - Beautiful
Wahine - Woman
Keiki - Child
Lani - Sky
Kane - Man

Home Sweet Home (page 76)

	Kickapoo	Pueblo	Sioux	Apache	Navajo	Iroquois	Seminoles
Buffalo Hide Tepee	X	X	Yes	X	X	X	X
Hogan	X	X	X	X	Yes	X	X
Wigwam	Yes	X	X	X	X	X	X
Longhouse	X	X	X	X	X	Yes	X
Brush Lodge	X	X	X	Yes	X	X	X
Adobe Village	X	Yes	X	X	X	X	X
Thatch Hut	X	X	X	X	X	X	Yes

Merry Christmas From Around the World (page 77)

Joyeux Noel - Switzerland
Um Feliz Natal - Portugal
Kung Ho Shen Tan - China
God Jul - Sweden
Stretan Bozic - Yugoslavia
Merry Christenmass - Scotland
Buon Natale - Italy
Wesolych Swiat - Poland
Feliz Navidad - Spain

Now That's Big! (page 78)

Dinosaur	Meters
Triceratops	10
Trachodon	13
Tyrannosaurus	15
Stegosaurus	6
Dimetrodon	3
Protoceratops	2
Diplodocus	29
Styracosaurus	5
Ankylosaurus	7

May I Borrow a Cup of Sugar, Please? (page 79)

Shampoo - Hindi
Ketchup - Malay
Alcohol - Arabic
Kindergarten - German
Souvenir - French
Coleslaw - Dutch
Squash - American Indian
Piano - Italian
Kosher - Yiddish
Smorgasbord - Scandinavian

You Are My Sunshine! (page 81)

You little angel.	He stole third base.
Dress the turkey.	I put my foot in my mouth.
Don't let the cat out of the bag.	My eyes are bigger than my stomach.

Dress the Turkey (page 82)

It's raining cats and dogs.	You're pulling my leg.	Hit the hay.
You are the apple of my eye.	There's a fork in the road.	My room is a pig pen.
I'm in hog heaven.	I'll be a monkey's uncle.	That's the way the cookie crumbles.

Get It Together (page 83)

1. bob
2. brain
3. bull
4. chain
5. check
6. child
7. back
8. box
9. corn
10. grand
11. ice
12. jack
13. walk
14. jump
15. book

Two Peas in a Pod (page 84)

1. 2 Peas in a Pod
2. 360 Degrees in a Circle
3. 206 Bones in the Body
4. 10 Dimes in a Dollar
5. 12 Eggs in a Dozen
6. 7 Continents on the Earth
7. 2 Sides to every Story
8. 4 Corners in a Square
9. 4 Chambers of the Heart
10. 9 Lives of the Cat
11. 144 Inches in a Square Foot
12. 2,000 Pounds in a Ton
13. 0 Calories in Water
14. 9 Saved by a Stitch In Time
15. 7 Digits in a Phone Number
16. 4 Singers in a Quartet
17. 5 Cards in a Poker Hand
18. 8 Arms on an Octopus
19. 8 Sides on a Stop Sign
20. 3 Wheels on a Tricycle

Eight Legs on a Spider (page 85)

1. 8 Legs on a Spider
2. 32 Ounces in a Quart
3. 100 Pennies in a Dollar
4. 3 Strikes and You're Out
5. 12 Months in a Year
6. 3 Little Pigs
7. 3 Sides on a Triangle
8. 9 Innings in a Base Ball Game (without Extra Innings)
9. 180 Degrees in a Straight Line
10. 1 Apple a Day Keeps the Doctor Away
11. 7 Dog Years to every Human Year
12. 50 Stars on the American Flag
13. 4 Quarts in a Gallon
14. 50 or 100 Yards in a dash
15. 8 Maids a Milking
16. 100 Yards on a Football Field
17. 4 Presidents on Mt. Rushmore
18. 5 Chinese Brothers
19. 4 Major Food Groups
20. 9 Months of Pregnancy